A Magna Colour Guide

Natural Beauty Care
With Flowers and Plants

A Magna Colour Guide

Natural Beauty Care
With Flowers and Plants

B. Hlava, F. Pospíšil and F. Starý

MAGNA BOOKS

Contents

Text by B. Hlava, F. Starý and F. Pospíšil
Illustrated by Z. Krejčová
Translated by V. Kratochvílová
Graphic design by I. Ouhel

This edition published 1995 by Magna Books
Magna Road, Wigston, Leicester LE18 4ZH
and produced in co-operation with Arcturus Publishing Limited

© 1990 Aventinum, Prague
First published 1981 by Artia, Prague

ISBN 1 85422 824 2
Printed in Slovakia by Neografia, Martin
3/99/34/51-02

Introduction

To gain and preserve health and fitness until advanced age is a natural wish of every human being, as is the desire to retain one's youthful looks for as long as possible. Since the beginning of history people have learned how to use a wide variety of preparations intended to beautify the body, and many of them have their origin in the plant world. Since ancient times plants have been the versatile helpers of human beings, who directly depend on them for their existence. The beauty and fragrance of plants have made an important contribution to human culture, and people have always used them in symbolic rituals as well as simply for personal adornment.

Since the plants used for cosmetic purposes are also very often used medicinally, the concepts of beauty and health have been inseparably connected. And, of course, no one can look good unless they have good health. Many herbal beauty aids can be taken internally to improve general health which will then benefit the appearance.

The curative properties of herbs have been discovered gradually over many centuries and the knowledge accumulated was passed on by oral tradition or in herbals. Plants or parts of plants have always been used in medicinal preparations designed for the treatment of simple ailments and also quite frequently of serious diseases, and even today these natural drugs are used, both in their original form and processed in various ways by modern chemical techniques. Numerous active chemical substances now produced synthetically were first found in plants, so the plant kingdom has played a very important part in the development of modern 'chemical' medicine which is based on the synthetic production of remedies.

Since plants contain active chemicals, however, it is important to realize that, while remedies and cosmetics from plants have the power to cure and help, they can also, if inappropriately used, do actual harm. This is why they should be used with care; they are not a panacea by which everything can be healed and cured.

Shortly after World War II the use of medicinal plants greatly increased and their importance for modern medicine was thereby demonstrated. Today, the use of these natural substances is more common in cosmetic products as well, partly as a reaction against the flooding of the market with products full of over-refined chemicals. Although synthetic chemicals are of course indispensable in the modern world it is preferable to use naturally occurring organic substances whenever possible as, when used correctly, they are less harmful to the body, simple to prepare, and in harmony with life.

Cosmetics

The word 'cosmetic' is of Greek origin, and means anything intended to care for the body in order to preserve or improve physical attractiveness and to remove or mask any defects. Modern cosmetics are developed on a scientific basis (cosmetology), implementing recent scientific medical, biological and chemical discoveries. The use and application of cosmetics to improve appearance is of course an art but, whether considered a science or an art, the preparation and use of cosmetics play an important part in our culture, by attempting to bring men and women nearer to their dream of an ideal of beauty.

Although cosmetics all have the same ultimate purpose, they are used in many different ways, from cleansing and protecting the skin and hair and painting the face to the treatment of various blemishes or defects. Cosmetics are by no means used consciously just for the purposes of being fashionable. Instinctively and subconsciously, we follow current ideals of beauty and we are also influenced by the looks of people around us, especially those we admire or respect. We have a need to be accepted by our peers and, being influenced by fashion and beauty culture to some extent, we are strongly affected by overt or concealed advertising and publicity, either directly, as a consumer yielding uncritically to this psychological pressure, or indirectly, by the example of people around us.

Individual taste is an important factor in the choice of cosmetic preparations, and manufacturers cater for this in a huge range of products. However, often the only difference between, say, one cream and another is the packaging. Nevertheless, the rule that the same thing does not suit everyone is true: one's skin type must be considered and, with make-up, one's age and colouring are also important.

Many cosmetics are used on both youthful and ageing skin for their protective or regenerative function, but no cosmetic used for skin care has the power to restore youth, as the manufacturers often try to persuade us. No doubt most of them are made in accordance with the basic rules of hygiene and have a more or less favourable effect on the skin, but their beneficial effect is limited, and will only be apparent if one is in good general health. It is not without reason that so much attention is devoted particularly to face cosmetics: the complexion reflects one's physical and mental health and well-being, and is a major factor in one's general good looks. As is now generally known, the complexion is unfavourably affected by too much coffee, alcohol and smoking. Less well known is the fact that drugs such as antibiotics, sleeping pills, tranquillizers and some contraceptive pills may be the cause of various rashes and pimples in susceptible people, and can bring about skin hypersensitivity.

Health and Beauty

As already mentioned, cosmetics have the best effect on healthy people. To achieve good health and reduce the risk of falling prey to every infection, it is important to take regular exercise, to get enough fresh air and sleep, as well as a balanced diet with the intake of calories equalling output. Being in the open air is easy enough for people living in the country or working out of doors, but most city-dwellers and office workers get their fresh air only at weekends. And getting sufficient sleep often seems to be a luxury in our busy lives. Nevertheless the consequences of lack of sleep, fresh air and exercise cannot be wiped out by several cups of coffee or even the best make-up.

Much has been written elsewhere about the problem of balanced calorie intake and output, and yet the number of overweight people in the western world is increasing, partly because of lack of exercise and partly because of overeating. An appropriate, wholesome diet is, however, simpler to achieve. Until the 19th century most of mankind was concerned with getting enough food but nowadays, in the western world at least, attention is being focused on the quality of food. The body needs proteins, carbohydrates, fats, mineral salts and vitamins, not only in the correct amounts but also in the correct proportions. We still do not know all the vital substances the body requires and this is why it is sensible to eat great number of different foods that preserve their natural composition as far as possible. We know that vegetables, fruit, eggs and dairy products all contain substances essential to health, and substances whose function in the body is still unknown. These are the main so-called protective foods and should all be included in the die regularly.

Many of the plants described in this book are used not only in cosmetics but also as essential elements of a balanced diet. For example oats, which have been cultivated for centuries and used as a staple food in many cultures, are rich in iron, calcium, magnesium, phosphorus and lecithin. They also contain numerous active substances such as glycosides, vitamins, enzymes, starch and proteins. Oats are also thought to contain certain substances with invigorating effects. Oatmeal as a soup or porridge is therefore considered an excellent food for patients or convalescents, and the polysaccharides they contain are known to have a favourable effect on gastric and intestinal inflammations and on the digestive system generally.

Body cleanliness, maintained by regular washing and bathing, also makes an important contribution to health and beauty. In different periods of history the significance of bathing has varied: in ancient Greece a cold, refreshing bath was an essential complement of gymnastics; in ancient Rome a bath was used to relax the body. Bathing has also been considered as a social event and was performed collectively. Today we think of bathing as

7

essential to modern life, mainly as a means of keeping clean. However, bathing has a favourable effect on the nervous system, blood circulation and metabolism, and therefore benefits the internal organs as well as the skin.

The effects of taking a bath, during which the blood flow through the internal organs is increased and nutrition of them improved, muscles become relaxed and pains are alleviated, make them useful for medicinal purposes. Baths with herbs added to the water are also used to treat various diseases; the chemical compounds contained in plants add to the effect of the water 'cure'. The earliest medicated baths were probably those made with plants.

The volatile oils, tannins and saponins, etc. contained in aromatic plants and woods help to refresh the skin surface, and their scent alone has a favourable effect on the bather. Many plants also have anti-inflammatory effects. A rosemary bath has a sedative effect which has proved successful in treating nervousness and exhaustion; lemon balm and lime flowers are added to the bath water to treat insomnia; and baths with willow bark are beneficial for skin diseases, frostbite, burns and rheumatism. An excellent mixture for simply refreshing and scenting the body consists of mint, arnica, lemon balm, rosemary and wild thyme.

A History of Cosmetics

The belief in the power of plants to improve the appearance, as well as to heal and cure, is as old as mankind itself. It was shared not only by the ancient Egyptians, Greeks and Romans but also by even older civilizations such as those of the American continent and Asia, where beauty care was highly developed thousands of years ago. In the Mediterranean region, yarrow, chamomile, butterbur, fragrant rose oil and various thyme species have been used for cosmetic purposes since early times.

People have always painted themselves, that is, made themselves up. At different times not only the face and lips but the whole body might be painted, as it is in some cultures today, for ritual or hygienic reasons as well as to correspond to the ideals of beauty of the period. Warriors would paint themselves with war paints, other paints would be used for the celebration of victory, others as a sign of mourning. Fragrant oils, ointments and balsams would also be smeared over the body, not only for their pleasant smell which gave a feeling of cleanliness and freshness, but to protect the skin against insects and bad weather.

Beautiful hair has long been appreciated — there is an old saying that the hair is one's crowning glory. Before the advent of modern shampoos and dyes, the hair was washed and tinted with herbal mixtures and herbal or vegetable dyes.

The World of Scents

When non-volatile perfumes, that is, those based on alcohol, were still unknown, various fragrant plant extracts were used as scents. The oils of the plants in these preparations evaporate readily and perfume the air; in rich households it was once common for tables, beds and floors to be strewn with fragrant herbs, either fresh, or dried and sprinkled with their own volatile oil.

In the Egyptian pyramids archaeologists have discovered vessels containing aromatic substances; if fragrances were given to the dead for their last journey it seems quite certain that they were used by the living, and this is confirmed in Homer's Iliad and Odyssey, which describe their heroes smearing their bodies with fragrant oils and perfumes. The cult of scents had developed so far by this time that a special scent was designed for each part of the body: the hair was anointed with marjoram, the face with palm oil, the neck with ivy essences, etc. The Romans also had a passion for scents: visitors to the Roman Coliseum would be sprinkled with fragrant water as they entered; and the emperor Caligula ordered decorative fruits filled with aromatic substances to be available at every feast.

Today we know that cleanliness is the first requirement in beauty care, but this was not always so. In the 17th century, for example, people wore elaborate clothes but little attention was paid to personal hygiene. Exquisite furniture and expensive draperies adorned the homes of the rich, but they had no bathrooms. Enormous periwigs were an essential part of fashionable dress, and these would inevitably become infested with lice, so the powder box and decorated scraper were necessary accompaniments. Scratching in public was perfectly acceptable, and the smelly consequences of bad hygiene were masked by the excessive use of perfume. (The first perfume factory was founded in 1608 by Dominican monks in Florence.)

One of the consequences of the French Revolution was that it put an end to this state of affairs: people began to dress less expensively, in simpler, more practical clothes, and personal hygiene gradually began to improve. The desire for scents remained, however, but they were used more sparingly to intensify the feeling of bodily cleanliness and freshness, and they still fulfil this function today. The mystique of an expensive fragrance, enclosed in a beautiful bottle bearing an exotic name, is alluring to millions, and even though you might consider perfume an unnecessary luxury, it is easy to be extravagant and succumb to its charm.

Warm climates encourage the formation of a high content of aromatic substances in plants. Such places as the Côte d'Azur between Nice and Marseilles are ideal for growing flowers for use in the perfume industry, and fields of roses, lavender and carnations are a common sight in such regions.

Besides plant and flower scents, perfume manufacturers had to rely until fairly recently on other fragrant substances obtained from animals, all of which are extremely rare and expensive. The best-known of them is musk, a substance secreted by several animals including the musk rat *(Ondatra zibethica)* and the musk deer *(Moschus moschiferus)*. Musk is one of the oldest perfume components. In the Orient, musk was used in an undiluted state. It was imported to Europe from Arabia and used as an ingredient of expensive perfumes, since it 'rounds up' the other scents in a perfume and keeps them stable. For a long time the production of synthetic musk was the dream of perfume manufacturers, and its discovery was a matter of a mere chance; during his experiments the man who was to invent nylon came across a substance with a very similar smell to that of musk.

Ambergris, found in the intestines of sperm whales *(Physeter catodon)*, is another ingredient of many perfumes, but it is very rare and therefore expensive, and its scent has also been created synthetically.

Another substance from the animal kingdom is civet, the glandular secretion of small cat-like carnivorous mammals called civets, native to Africa and Asia. Civet has a very penetrating smell and must be used in very weak dilutions. Another source of scent is the glandular secretion of beavers.

Artificial (synthetic) substances compose the third group of scents. These were sometimes discovered by chance, or appeared as a by-product of chemical production or as the result of the persistent endeavours of chemists. Chemists have succeeded in synthesizing a great number of plant and animal scents indispensable to the modern cosmetic industry. Nowadays even the cheapest shampoo or hair lotion is perfumed, usually synthetically. Yet, despite the undoubted achievements of chemistry, the basic substances found in plants still retain their popularity and are in fact irreplaceable.

It must be stressed that wearing perfumes successfully requires taste, sense and, most importantly, moderation. Here the principle that less is more applies. For the daytime it is best to use cologne which contains 2−4 per cent fragrant substances. For special occasions in the evening, perfumes containing 4−20 per cent fragrant substances are suitable. The choice of perfume is as important as the choice of jewelry and other accessories, since cologne and perfume, worn regularly become our 'signature', a part of our personality.

Perfumes based on simple fruit and flower scents are designed for the young, whereas scents of the same type but in more complex combinations are considered suitable for older women. The more daring usually choose spicy perfumes, while exotic essences are designed for women of refinement and elegance. It must not be forgotten that perfume should complement the personality rather than dominate it; its purpose is merely to add the final touch to the natural scent of our clean and well-kept exterior.

10

Parts of Plants Used in Cosmetics and Their Forms

Most cosmetically important aromatic plants are grown only in tropical climates, others grow in subtropical regions, and others in temperate zones. Even in cool climates there is a surprisingly large number of plants useful in cosmetics and perfumery. These include woodruff, primrose, cowslip, violet, lime, nettle, hop and flax. Some of these plants grow in fertile lowlands, others on mountains and others in or near water. They are either gathered from the wild or cultivated. As fresh plants are liable to rapid decay, the valuable substances which they contain are preserved by drying or extraction. Plant extracts form such substances as agar, resins, volatile oils and balms.

There is practically no difference between plants gathered from the wild and cultivated ones. The assumption that drugs from wild plants are more effective is incorrect and there are numerous species that grow only in cultivation, in fields or gardens. What is essential is that the plants used are healthy, without fungal or virus diseases, clear of dust or soil, and not contaminated by herbicides or pesticides which leave poisonous residues in the plants. Successful cultivation of aromatic and medicinal plants also requires a knowledge of their biology and their environmental needs. It is important to know which part of the plant is harvested for use. Active or aromatic substances are only occasionally distributed in the whole plant; more often they are found only in some of its parts. Usually only the part with the highest concentration of such substances is gathered. The best manner and time of gathering are also of importance.

There are various systems of classifying plant material. The most common is the organographic system, which classifies the plant raw material according to the part of the plant gathered. From the parts of the plant above the ground the following are gathered:

herb *(herba)*	flower *(flos)*
bud *(gemma)*	seed *(semen)*
bark *(cortex)*	stalk *(caulis)*
stipe *(stipes)*	wood *(lignum)*
spores *(sporae)*	fruit *(fructus)*
leaf *(folium)*	glands *(glandulae)*

From the subterranean parts of plants the following are gathered:

root *(radix)*	rhizome *(rhizoma)*
bulb *(bulbus)*	tuber *(tuber)*

11

One of the oldest and best-known medicinal and cosmetic plants is wild chamomile. The flowers are the part used for the preparation of infusions and extracts or for distillation of volatile oil. The main active component of the volatile oil is the blue-coloured azulene called in this instance chamazulene. Besides chamazulene, chamomile contains numerous other therapeutically valuable substances. Since ancient times it has been used to soothe sensitive skin, and in general for its anti-inflammatory effects. Most cosmetic manufacturers use it in creams, shampoos, skin milks and lotions, and a decoction is used for gargling in cases of toothache, and for indigestion. It is also used in dermatology in compresses and baths for the treatment of various skin diseases.

Another example of a herb used as a skin treatment is agrimony. The dried flowers are used in the form of a decoction for baths and compresses, as for dried chamomile.

Dried burdock root, which contains volatile oils, tannins, mucilage and mineral substances, is used for promoting hair growth. Although its effect has not yet been reliably demonstrated, it is nevertheless still used on the basis of old folk wisdom and experience.

Another plant which has proved successful in cosmetic care is the hop. This climbing plant is usually thought of as an ingredient in beer, and is cultivated for that purpose, but it also grows wild in thickets and on river banks. It contains not only lupulin which gives beer its taste and durability, but also volatile oils, tannins and hormones (oestrogens). In cosmetic treatment hops are used to soothe irritated skin and can be added to the bath for that purpose. Its fluid extract is used in skin and hair lotions and shampoos. The oestrogens contained in hops influence skin metabolism and are believed to have rejuvenating effects.

The plants used in beauty care and cosmetics are used in various forms. Ideally, one should use fresh plant juices, since they contain the active substances in their fullest strength. Unfortunately they rapidly deteriorate and this is why they are not often used in commercial preparations. But they can of course be used at home. Freshly squeezed carrot, cucumber, tomato and lemon juice are all effective: after their application the skin is rehydrated, toned up and becomes more elastic. Consequently, the skin becomes finer, refreshed and its general appearance improves.

Not only fresh juice but also plants preserved by drying may be used in beauty care. Carefully dried plants retain their active constituents and have a wide range of applications. From dried plants infusions and decoctions are prepared. In an infusion the extract is obtained by pouring boiling water on the herb; in a decoction the herb is added to water and boiled. Infusions and decoctions are then strained through a fine sieve before use.

Plants in the Manufacture of Modern Cosmetics

Even the broadest commercially made cosmetic assortment is far from being complete. Each of us has individual requirements and it is not always easy to meet them with bought products, and so there is a good reason for beauty care using home-made preparations. And for such home cosmetics plants are invaluable raw materials. Every plant is in fact a very intricate factory producing active substances, which, though chemically complex, are perfectly synthetised by the plant and are, moreover, cheap and easily available. These substances are natural products produced by a living organism, biologically acceptable to man. This of course does not mean that all synthetic, artificial compounds developed by man are less good. However, there are risks attached to the excessive use of chemicals. Man, dazzled by his capacity to synthetise chemicals, tended to forget that living nature has always been able to accomplish syntheses which are just as marvellous, much more intricate, and far cheaper. Thanks to the development of organic chemistry and pharmacology, we are able to determine which useful substances are produced by a plant and what effects these substances have on the body, so it seems sensible and progressive to use natural plant extracts in beauty preparations, manufactured as well as home-made. Many world-famous cosmetic manufacturers now use natural ingredients in many of their products.

Skin Cosmetics

Soaps are manufactured by neutralization of fatty acids with a lye. In water soap yields a lather that releases dirt from the skin and removes dust and dead cells from the skin surface. Cosmetic soaps, the so-called neutral toilet soaps with a high unsaponified fat-content, are used. Toilet soaps prevent defattening of the skin, although their effectiveness in this depends on the amount of fatty acids they contain. Toilet soaps are usually perfumed and dyed, either synthetically or with natural products. Cosmetic soaps can also contain plant extracts such as chamomile, sage, etc. Besides toilet soaps, medicated soaps containing borax, sulphur or tar, for example, are manufactured.

Creams are usually made from plant oils (such as olive and almond oils, and cacao butter) or animal fats (such as lard, lanolin obtained from sheep's wool, and spermaceti). Mineral fats such as vaseline are less suitable for cosmetic purposes, as they do not penetrate the skin and protect only the surface. Paraffin, however, is an exception, and is suitable for the preparation of face

13

packs. Creams are perfumed with manufactured scents or natural volatile oils, and can be of dense or thin consistency. The so-called emulsion creams, prepared by the dispersion of fat particles into water, are very useful, as they are pleasant to apply and have a more pronounced effect due to their capacity of penetrating deeper into the skin (helping to prevent the premature formation of wrinkles). Rich creams, half-dry creams and dry creams differ only in the amount of fat they contain. Extra-rich creams have a good cleansing capacity and are also used as night creams, predominantly on dry skin.

Greasy skin needs little if any cream. As a day cream dry cream is best, as it makes the cleansing of the skin easier. Application of all types of cream has a single aim — to preserve or restore the elasticity and softness of the skin, thus enhancing its appearance. Hydrating creams gently moisten the skin while nutrition creams supply it with vitamins and hormones. Vitamins can also be supplied to the skin by means of creams with fruit or vegetable extracts. Apricot, orange, lemon, banana, strawberry, peach, grapevine, tomato, cucumber and carrot juices are all used. Other plant juices such as aloe benefit ageing skin and are used in creams. There is a broad variety of sun-tan creams too, ranging from the purely protective to those containing active, pigmentation-producing substances, and into these creams substances of natural origin such as walnut are very often added. And natural substances such as menthol or camphor are often a part of massage creams.

Powders are manufactured from raw materials of natural origin, such as starches or lycopodium spores, or from mineral raw materials, such as zinc oxide or talc. Mineral powders are most suitable for covering spots and pimples, as they do not swell up and are not a cultivation medium for pathological microorganisms. In cosmetics mixed powders made of both plant and mineral raw materials are the most common. Powders are dyed to the required shade with synthetic dyes, which can be given more precise nuances of shade than natural ones. For perfuming, mostly synthetic compositions in the quantities from $0.1-0.2$ per cent in loose and 1 per cent in compact powders are used.

The main functions of face powder are to mask cosmetic defects such as wrinkles, scars and blemishes, and to give a mat, smooth surface to the skin. Medicinal powders contain mixtures of therapeutic substances. Powders in paste or cream form and known as foundation are also frequently used.

Basically, there are three main types of make-up, classified according to consistency, as liquid (make-up fluids), pastes (make-up crème) and powders. Eye-shadows, mascaras, lipsticks, nail polishes, and all other make-up preparations may be classified in this way. Besides the basic substances responsible for their consistency, they contain adjusting elements in various shades and of various physical properties responsible for the resulting appearance of the make-up on the skin. Transparent make-ups suitable for every skin type and in different colour shades must have the following properties: easy application, stability (the make-up must not be liable to changes with variations of temperature), an ability to maintain skin moisture without limiting its natural formation, reliability (it must not crack or scale off) and a mat, velvet-like, natural look. Special preparations of this type include sun-tan make-ups, which underline and brighten the features of a sun-tanned face. Before the application of make-ups the skin must be perfectly clean and a suitable base cream, chosen according to skin type, must be applied. The cream fixes the make-up and prevents sebum secretion and perspiration, which causes the make-up to alter on the skin. No biologically active substances, not even plant extracts, are added to skin make-up.

Lipsticks, eye-shadows, blushers and other cosmetic products of purely decorative character require pristine laboratories, raw materials and hygienic production methods. All of them are also manufactured from synthetic raw materials only.

Face lotions, used as skin cleansers and toners, are manufactured from diluted (10−50 per cent) ethanol with the admixture of glycerine. The greasier the skin, the higher the concentration of ethanol it tolerates. Face lotions often have plant extracts with anti-inflammatory, fungicidal, astringent and soothing effects added to them. These plant extracts also serve to perfume face lotions; for this refreshing, simple, light compositions (0.25−1 per cent) are common. The terpenes must be removed from volatile oils to avoid skin irritation, before being used in face lotions. Such preparations can be homemade, for example by extracting a mixture of equal parts of dried chamomile and sage (10 g of each) with 100 g of 20 per cent ethanol. Such a face lotion has excellent cleansing and anti-inflammatory effects. An ethanol-free face lotion, prepared from the juice of freshly grated cucumbers, is more suitable for sensitive skin, and an application of fresh tomato juice, with its pronounced tonic effects, is beneficial for tired skin. Aftershave lotions, with their marked disinfectant and refreshing character, and colognes, with their aesthetic rather than cosmetic significance, may also be classed as face lotions.

Skin milks are emulsions of two types, either water-in-oil or oil-in-water. As skin milks are used mainly for cleansing dry, sensitive skin, they are not perfumed with irritating volatile oils. They do, however, frequently contain plant components such as azulene from chamomile or wheat germ extract.

Face packs are extraordinarily effective cosmetic treatments. They can be made of many different ingredients, so that every woman can choose her individual skin-care strategy, with the possibility of using a variety of natural substances in their preparation. If appropriately used they nourish, soften and refresh the skin, increase its elasticity and remove impurities and small imperfections. Face packs have effects which can include refining, nourishing, astringent, depigmentating, drying or moistening. Lanolin, paraffin, hot oil, egg yolk, mayonnaise, yolk-and-honey mixtures, yeast, vegetable and fruit packs may all be used. To prepare and apply homemade face packs the following rules must be followed:

a) The raw materials must be fresh and of very good quality. Dried-out carrot or bad tomatoes, lemons or bananas, for example, will not do.

b) Face packs must be prepared immediately before use. Only stainless steel utensils should be used for cutting or grating, and either porcelain or glass vessels should be used.

c) Before the application of the face pack a facial steam and possibly a light massage are a good idea.

d) When the face pack is applied it is necessary to take a complete rest, without speaking or reading.

e) A single pack application will do little good: it must be repeated several times.

f) With warm packs it is a good idea to wrap the face in a dry cloth in order to retain the heat.

g) With packs that remain liquid and must not solidify (oil, vegetable and fruit-based packs) it is advisable to use soaked cotton wool or gauze filled with the vegetable or fruit pulp, or oil.

h) Eyes, mouth and nostrils should not be covered with the pack.

Some less common face packs include the following:

Chamomile Cleansing and Anti-inflammatory Pack
In a clean porcelain dish 100 g of chamomile flowers are poured over with boiling water to form a mash, and left for 10 minutes. The mash is then spread over strips of gauze which are placed across the forehead, cheeks, nose, chin and throat. The pack is left on the face until it cools (approximately 20 minutes). Before applying the pack, a moisturizer should be applied to dry skin and wiped off after removing the face pack.

Lemon Astringent Cleansing Pack
A paste made with milk, lemon pulp and wheat flour is applied to the face and allowed to dry. After 20 minutes the face is washed with warm chamomile extract (50 g to half a litre of water).

Astringent Pack from Tea Extract
Cotton wool pads are soaked with a strong extract of brewed, strained tea

16

and applied hot to the face for 20 minutes, after which the face should be washed with lukewarm water.

Nutritious Strawberry Pulp Pack

Strawberries are pulped and mixed with milk and cooked mashed potatoes to make a paste. It should be left on the face for 30 minutes and then washed off with lukewarm chamomile extract or lukewarm water.

Nutritious Yeast Pack with Carrots

Yeast is finely crumbled in milk, and grated carrot and a few drops of olive oil are added to make a paste. After 20 minutes the pack is removed and the face is washed with warm water.

Refreshing Fruit Pulp Packs

For these packs apricot, banana, strawberry or tomato pulp mixed with egg white (two table-spoonfuls of pulp to one egg white) and thickened with wheat flour can be used. It should be left on the face for 15—20 minutes, then removed and the face washed with lukewarm water.

Bath additives are usually bath salts, oils, or foams in which the foaming capacity of saponins is utilized. Baths are important both from the point of view of general hygiene and of cosmetic care of the body. Here, too, various herbs with invigorating, cleansing and anti-inflammatory effects can be used as ingredients. Immediately before the bath the herbal essence in the form of an infusion or decoction is prepared and poured into the bath water. Suitable herb-baths include infusions of chamomile, yarrow, sage or agrimony, and decoctions of oak bark, willow bark or birch leaves. For one bath you will need about two litres of an infusion or decoction made from 0.5 kg of the plant. A mixed infusion of, for example, chamomile, hop, balm, fennel and yarrow may also be used.

Hair cosmetics. This group comprises such commercial preparations as dyes, tints, setting lotions, hair sprays, shampoos, conditioners, brilliantines and hair oils. Many hair cosmetics contain natural substances such as birch-tree sap, and extracts of chamomile, stinging nettle, hop, onion or mistletoe. A chamomile infusion, which may easily be used at home, has the effect of improving the colour of fair hair and making dark hair lighter. A strong infusion made from 100 to 200 g of the herb to 500 cc of water should be used. Other harmless natural tints used for the hair are henna and indigo (for more details see under Henna, page 136).

Cosmetics for the mouth. This group comprises toothpastes and mouth-washes. In general, natural substances with disinfective, deodorizing and anti-inflammatory properties are effective; such substances are menthol from mint, thymol from thyme, anethol from anise, and volatile oils such as clove, eucalyptus, fennel and cinnamon. Mouthwashes often contain plant tinctures (ethanol extracts), especially benzoin tincture from storax *(Styrax benzoin)*, myrrh tincture from *Commiphora abyssinica* and rhatang tincture from *Krameria triandra*. Chlorophyll – the natural green colouring matter of plants – is also frequently used.

Perfumes are not cosmetics in the true sense of the word, yet they are an important ingredient in cosmetic products. Natural volatile oils as well as chemically synthetised imitations of natural products are used. Manufacturers combine the individual fragrances into blends, an art which originated in France about 300 years ago. Perfumes are composed using four types of scent. These are the basic substances (which give the perfume its main scent), nuancers (by means of which the basic scent is refined), effective substances (giving the scent its unique character), and fixatives or stabilizers (which harmonize and blend everything into a stable, unchanging whole).

Active Substances of Plants

For those who want more detailed information on why so many plants have a favourable influence on our appearance this section dealing with the active substances of plants is added; it will be necessary to touch upon the complex world of organic chemistry. This will be mentioned only briefly, as the biochemical processes that take place in plants are extremely complicated and in many cases their details are still unknown. The chemical compounds contained in plants, the active substances, are usually concentrated in large amounts in certain parts of a plant, and the amount varies according to the age of the plant and the climatic conditions and soil in which it grew.

Active substances in plants can be very roughly divided into two groups. The first one comprises substances essential for the plant as building materials and sources of energy; such substances are the products of primary metabolism. They include saccharides, from monosaccharides through alcoholic saccharides and oligosaccharides to polysaccharides, organic acids, fatty acids and their compounds (that is, lipids, oils and waxes), amino acids, peptides and proteins, including enzymes. The other group includes products of secondary metabolism. From the chemical point of view these substances are usually more complex, and are probably not vital for the plant, having rather the character of excretions or reserve substances which the plant uses only occasionally. The plant can do quite well without them, without any harm to its basic vital metabolic processes. Among the products of secondary metabolism are glycosidic compounds including coumarine derivatives, lignans, terpenes, steroids and saponins, bitter substances, volatile oils, resins

18

and balms, tannins and alkaloids. Of the above groups, which contain thousands of complicated chemical substances, it is only necessary to mention those having the most use in beauty care.

Products of Primary Metabolism

Carbohydrates

Monosaccharides are sugars with a simple molecule which cannot be split by hydrolysis. To these belong glucose (grape sugar), fructose (fruit sugar), contained in fruit and honey and often used in various face packs, and D-mannitol, an alcoholic sugar contained in manna, the solidified natural exudation of the manna ash *(Fraxinus ornus)*, which also forms part of some face packs.

Oligosaccharides are sugars with a molecule consisting of two or more monosaccharides. They include sucrose (cane sugar), obtained from sugar cane or sugar beet, maltose, a sugar contained in malt and malt extracts, and lactose (milk sugar). Their use in cosmetics is limited to skin nutrients; they are more often used in preparations used internally for skin eruptions, as well as for improving the general condition of convalescents.

Polysaccharides have a very large molecule and are carbohydrates that have little in common with sugars. The group contains galactans from marine algae (agar or carrageen), frequently used in cosmetics for the preparation of gels and emulsions, for stabilizing the consistency of creams and ointments and for special face packs. Mucilages and gums are polysaccharides able to form a protective film on the mucous membranes and skin, useful in cases of skin inflammation. Another group of polysaccharides – the starches – are used as the basis of various powders. Starch grains of different sizes are selected as required. The most common one is rice starch.

Organic Acids

These comprise the following acids: malic, citric, succinic, tartaric, acetic and oxalic. The malic, tartaric and citric acids in fruit are the most important cosmetically. They are believed to have a 'blood-cleansing' effect, and are of great importance in gels, creams and face packs, as skin cleansers and strengtheners, and for improving blood circulation and refining the skin. Fruit pulps used in face packs contain, besides these acids, vitamin complexes, particularly vitamin C, and also A_1, B_1 and B_2.

Fatty Acids and Their Compounds – Oils and Fats

The substances included in this group are cosmetically important in themselves and also for mixing with other active substances. Many vegetable oils

19

(such as olive, almond, avocado and sesame) and butters (coconut and cocoa) are widely used in cosmetics. Their function is to protect the skin and soothe irritation. They are therefore used in rich moisturizers, skin milks, face packs and soaps. Substances of a lipoid character such as lecithin from egg yolk (often used in packs and shampoos) and stigmasterol (a vegetable lipoid which forms a provitamin D with an excellent effect on the skin) are chemically very close to fats. Carotenes from carrot, red beet and hips are the preliminary stages of provitamin A. The significance of vitamins for health justifies the enriching cosmetics with vitamins.

Amino Acids, Proteins and Enzymes

These are the most important substances of living organisms. At present 21 amino acids are known; they are the basic substances from which proteins are built. Enzymes are particularly important proteins that act as catalysts of all vital processes. Most amino acids, peptides and proteins, including enzymes, can be isolated and used. For example, in the dairy industry such milk products as curd cheese, whey, kefir, and buttermilk are all obtained by enzymatic reactions. These are used for the preparation of some face packs. The plant enzymes papain, ficin and bromelin, isolated from the milky sap of papaya *(Carica papaya),* various fig species (e. g. *Ficus glabra*) and pineapples *(Ananas comosus),* are not only excellent digestive enzymes but also have an anti-inflammatory effect when used in cosmetics. Amino acids are constituents of antibiotics, used in the control of infectious diseases including those of the skin. Proteins, together with lipids and saccharides, are the main substances contained in yeasts, which are also rich in vitamins. Yeast packs are very important in beauty care, as they act not only as skin strengtheners and astringents but also as suppliers of the important B-group vitamins, known for their beneficial effect on acne.

Products of Secondary Metabolism

Glycosides

These are natural organic substances consisting of sugar and non-sugar components. Of the glycosides, saponins are especially valuable in beauty care. Shaken up with water they lather profusely, and this capacity, along with their antifungal effect, is utilized in the making of baths. Taken internally, many of them are toxic, while others have excellent therapeutic effects. Other glycosides used include the phenolic glycoside salicin from willow bark, used for inflammation and swellings, and those with a photosensitive effect, used in sun-tan creams to enhance pigmentation.

20

Volatile Oils

These are natural liquid substances of oily consistency, usually pleasantly fragrant even in very small quantities. They are volatile, that is, they evaporate rapidly, and, while insoluble in water, they are soluble in ethanol and other organic solvents. In plants volatile oils are found in special oil-bearing cells, glands and intercellular spaces.

Of the 295 plant families, about a third include plants that contain volatile oils in industrially usable quantities. Volatile oils are the basis of scents and flavourings. Their wide use in perfumery indicates their special significance for cosmetics: of the world annual production of volatile oils − over 200 thousand tons − about one third is used for perfumery. In cosmetics, especially in low-percentage colognes and skin lotions, deterpened volatile oils are used. The terpenic components of volatile oils are hydrocarbons which have no scent and rather impair their quality. This is why they are removed from the volatile oils by the process called deterpenation.

Balms and Resins

Balms and resins are the products of injured or diseased plants and are related to volatile oils. The plant usually produces them after an injury to the surface tissues. Resins are solid and balms liquid (being actually resins combined with volatile oils). Resins as well as volatile oils are used in mouthwashes and toothpastes. Some balms, such as Peruvian balsam, are added to soaps and ointments for soothing and healing purposes.

Tannins

Tannins are unstable, nitrogen-free substances, easily oxidizing, polymerizing and forming insoluble complexes. This is why tannin-containing plants stored for a long time are less effective than fresh ones. Their use in cosmetics is determined by their pronounced astringent effect, caused by their reaction with skin proteins. Under the influence of tannins a protective membrane is formed on damaged skin, the nerve endings are desensitized, the discharge of secretions is stopped and inflammations as well as irritation and itching are reduced. Because of its high content of tannins, an infusion of tea is useful cosmetically for washing the skin. This is the only one of the large group of alkaloid-containing plants (in this case caffeine) recommended for cosmetic use, as in all the others the alkaloids penetrating into the blood flow are poisonous to humans.

Finally, it must be stated that the individual active substances contained in plants do not act separately but in an interdependent way, by complex chemical reactions.

21

Mimosa

Leguminosae

Acacia farnesiana Willd.

Description: A profusely branched spiny shrub reaching a height of 3−4 m. Branches with short, sharp, straight spines. Leaves double pinnate, composed of small leaflets. Subtropical species, with high temperature requirement during its period of growth. Flowers from autumn to early spring. Flower size 12−15 mm. Flowers are deep yellow, arranged in axillary globose inflorescences (heads). From two to three inflorescences grow from each older branch axil on pappose pedicels. Flower scent intense, pleasant, resembling violets. Fruit is a 3−7 cm long pod containing flat seeds.

Origin and Distribution: Probably native to Central America, but it has long been grown in the Farnese gardens in Rome, which gave it its scientific name. Nowadays cultivated in southern France, Algeria, Egypt, Syria, India, Australia and southern USA.

Preparation: Its volatile oil is extracted from the flowers with petroleum ether: from 1,000 kg of fresh flowers only 1,800 g volatile oil is obtained, which makes it expensive. Whereas in 1900 35 tons of flowers were processed in France, the present production is considerably lower, as the less profitable natural raw material has been increasingly replaced by synthetic products. Other fragrant acacias, such as *Acacia cavenia* Hook. et Arn. or *Acacia dealbata* Lk. have shared the same fate.

Constituents: The volatile oil (0.5−0.7 per cent) contains methylester of salicylic acid, p-cresol, benzaldehyde, cuminic aldehyde and geraniol.

Cosmetic Uses: Volatile oils used for the preparation of perfumes which are very expensive, as the price of natural volatile oils is high.

Other Uses: In mid-winter (January) florists sell the fragrant blooming twigs of 'mimosa' which is also a popular ornamental shrub in warm regions. In the temperate zone it is grown only in greenhouses, as it does not tolerate temperatures below −6° C.

Yarrow

Compositae

Achillea millefolium L.

Description: A perennial plant with creeping rootstock; from it grow basal pinnately divided leaves and flower-bearing stems. Stems about 50 cm high, erect, densely foliate, woolly, branching into a convex or flat capitula arranged in loose cymes. Flowers mostly white, sometimes pink. Flowering from June to September. It has a pleasant, slightly bitter smell.

Origin and Distribution: Common throughout Europe, Asia (as far as to the western part of the Himalayas) and America. Grows on dry meadows, balks and pastureland in lowlands as well as mountains.

Harvesting and Preparation: The heads or the whole herb are gathered during the flowering period, sometimes only the leaves or rhizomes. Dried in shade at the temperature to 40° C.

Constituents: The flowering herb contains volatile oil (0.25 per cent) rich in various components (a mixture of monoterpenic and sesquiterpenic carbo-hydrates, mainly chamazulene − 40 per cent), bitter substances with the proazulene achilline, saturated and unsaturated carbohydrates, lower fatty acids, phytosterols, guaianolids, germacranolids, etc. These complex substances have spasmolytic and antibacterial effects and regulate digestion disorders.

Cosmetic Uses: Yarrow extract forms part of stabilized plant extracts which suppress skin inflammation, facilitate skin cleansing, remove dead cells from the skin, restrict sebum secretion and help close the pores. Consequently, yarrow extracts are added to regenerative and soothing creams, skin lotions and face packs, toothpastes and mouthwashes, and shampoos and hair conditioners. Yarrow extract (5 spoonfuls of the dried herb are decocted with 0.5 l water for 30 minutes) is excellent for the skin. It can also be used as a hair rinse for greasy hair and dandruff. For chronic eczemas yarrow extract may be added to the bath (1:10).

Other Uses: Yarrow has many medicinal uses. Its healing effects were described by the ancient scholars Hippocrates, Pliny and Dioscurides, and also by the medieval scholar Abbess Hildegard.

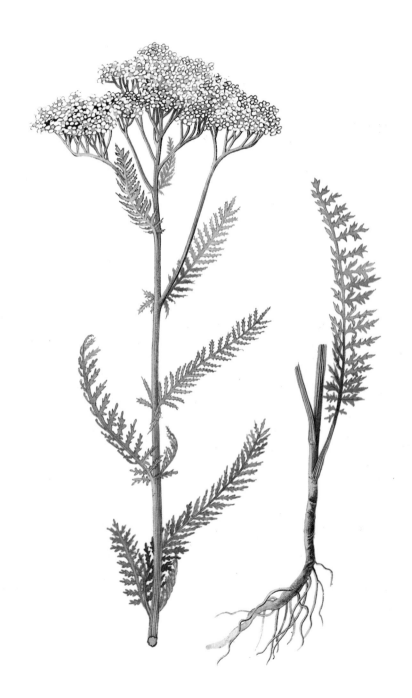

Sweet Flag
Acorus calamus L.

Araceae

Description: A robust perennial plant, up to 150 cm high, with a creeping rootstock, up to 3 cm thick and 50 cm long. From the rootstock rise sword-like leaves 1 m long and triangular, simple stems. The stems terminate in a spadix of tiny flowers, first green, later light brown. In Europe sweet flag is propagated solely by rhizomes.

Origin and Distribution: Native to swampy mountainous regions of India, it nowadays grows wild in temperate zones of Asia, Europe and America, in marshes, on the banks of ponds and brooks, and in damp ditches. Not usually cultivated; the rootstocks of wild growing plants are gathered.

Harvesting and Preparation: Gathered in autumn, during its second or third year. After thorough cleaning the rhizomes are cut into pieces and dried in shade or artificially, at temperatures up to 40° C. It is not advisable to peel the rhizomes, as in this way much volatile oil is wasted. The drug has a pungent, aromatic smell and spicy bitter taste.

Constituents: The rootstocks contain 2−6 per cent volatile oil which is very aromatic and of variable composition, but usually of terpenes and sesquiter-penes. The characteristic component of the volatile oil is asaron (10 per cent) which affects the central nervous system (halucinogenic effects are similar to those of myristicin from nutmeg); in higher doses it may be toxic. Besides volatile oil the drug contains bitter substances and tannins which are of cosmetic importance.

Cosmetic Uses: Sweet flag is used as a bath ingredient, as it stimulates and disinfects the skin by promoting the blood flow to the skin. A bath prepared by adding 50 cc ethanol extract of sweet flag to 30 l water is very refreshing and invigorating. Calamus extract, as it is sometimes called, has a limited use as a scent for soap.

The disinfectant and deodorizing effect is also made use of: ethanol extracts of sweet flag or the volatile oil itself are added to mouthwashes; the volatile oil is used to flavour chewing gum.

Other Uses: In folk medicine sweet flag is used to improve digestion and regulate disorders of the digestive tract. It is either drunk in the form of an infusion or taken in powder form before meals.

26

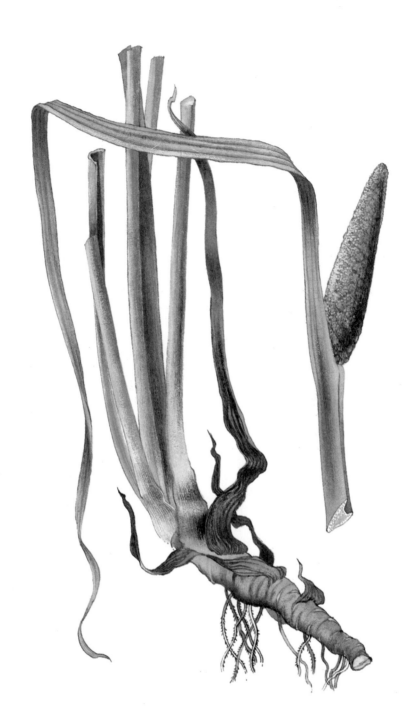

Agrimony

Rosaceae

Agrimonia eupatoria L.

Description: A perennial plant up to 1 m high, with a short woody rhizome and stem covered with coarse hairs. Leaves unpaired pinnate, composed of oblong ovoid, serrate leaflets, with grey hairs on the reverse. Tiny yellow flowers, mostly arranged in simple, spiky racemes 10−30 cm long. Flowering from June to August.

Distribution: A rather variable species with numerous forms distributed throughout the whole of Europe, northern Africa and central Asia. It grows in deciduous woodland, on pastureland, in thickets, ditches and clearings, from lowlands to mountains.

Harvesting and Preparation: The flowering herb is gathered from June to August and dried in shade or artificially, at temperatures not exceeding 40° C. For external use the fresh, ground herb may be used.

Constituents: Agrimony contains 5−8 per cent tannins, flavone glycosides, acids, traces of volatile oil, vitamin C and other little-known substances, with disinfectant and healing effects.

Cosmetic Uses: An infusion of agrimony mixed with diluted ethanol is used for cleansing greasy skin, skin with dilated pores and acne-affected skin. The organic acids cleanse the skin and the tannins act astringently to help close the pores. Its disinfectant effects benefit inflamed spots. As a face pack, an agrimony infusion mixed with peat can be used. The resulting paste is applied to the face, and afterwards the face is washed with a chamomile infusion. In a peat pack the healing, cleansing and astringent effects of agrimony combine with the hormonal regenerative effects of peat. Agrimony treatments are not suitable for dry and sensitive skin, as sometimes an allergic reaction (reddening or a rash) may result.

Other Uses: The flowering herb is used for the preparation of an infusion (10 g per 1/4 l water) which is drunk as tea for lack of appetite, and gall-bladder or gastric diseases. It may also be added to the bath to aid the healing of wounds.

Onion
Allium cepa L.

Liliaceae

Description: A biennial to triennial plant with a spherical or flat-spherical bulb serving as storage organ for the plant, formed during the first or second year. Shallow roots growing only in the upper layers of the topsoil. Leaves round, rod-like, pointed, dark green, waxy pruinose, shorter than the flower-bearing stem which attains 60−110 cm in the second year. The stem terminates in an umbel of whitish-green flowers on long pedicels. Fruit is a capsule.

Origin and Distribution: Wild forms are found in the mountains of Afghanistan, Iran and Turkestan; it is therefore very probable that the common onion comes from western Asia. Excavations have demonstrated that the onion has been cultivated from ancient times, and was even considered sacred. Onions were known and used in ancient Egypt, China, eastern India and Asia Minor.

Constituents: Like the garlic, chive and leek, the onion is an important medicinal plant because of its high content of pungent volatile oil with organically bound sulphur. It has a pronounced disinfectant, antibacterial and fungicidal effect. The use of onion in cosmetics is not based solely on its volatile oil content but on other components such as fructose, flavone derivatives, vitamins B_1, B_2 and C, pantothenic acid and carotene, which have nutritious and regenerative effects.

Cosmetic Uses: The sulphur content is used in the preparation of shampoos, as it restricts excessive sebum secretion and dandruff formation, and encourages blood circulation in the scalp, which is also favourably affected by the vitamin content. Extracts of onion, nettle, birch and mistletoe all form part of various hair treatments. Reddish-brown dry onion skins can be used for hair tinting: 30 g skins are boiled in 200 ml water and, after filtering off, 5 g glycerin is added. The preparation is applied to the hair daily until the required colour is obtained. This treatment is, however, unsuitable for greasy hair.

Other Uses: One of the most widespread cultivated plants, mainly used as a vegetable.

Common Alder

Betulaceae

Alnus glutinosa (L.) Gaertn.

Description: A deciduous tree more than 20 m high; leaves round, dentate. Young leaves, especially in open buds, are sticky. Flowers in catkins, the male catkins pendulous, the female catkins erect, reddish-purple, developing into small, woody, spherical cones growing from the leaf axils.

Origin and Distribution: Native to Europe, Siberia, northern Africa and Asia Minor; introduced to North America. Prefers cool, moist habitats, but tolerates partial shade.

Harvesting and Preparation: Young leaves or buds are gathered in spring and dried in shade.

Constituents: Young leaves contain organic acids, saccharides, tannins, mineral salts and numerous, little-known, glycoside-bound compounds. An infusion of the leaves has an effect similar to that of the birch leaves, that is, diuretic and diaphoretic.

Cosmetic Uses: An infusion of 50 g of the leaves to half a litre of boiling water can be used externally as hair rinse, especially in cases of increased hair loss, excessive dandruff and discharge of sebum, but should not be applied more than once a week. Between each treatment an extract of birch or nettle with alcohol may be applied at night. An infusion of alder leaves or buds gathered in spring and mixed with oat flour to make a stiff paste can be used as a face pack with a very good cleansing effect. After its application the skin tightens and the blood flow to the skin is increased. It also helps to unclog the pores and reduce inflammation. After removing the pack it is advisable to apply a nutritious half-dry cream and gently rub it into the skin.

Other Uses: The soft, pliable and easily split wood is suitable for carving and is used in water constructions, such as in the manufacture of wooden pumps.

Lemon Verbena

Verbenaceae

Alcysia triphylla (L'Herit.) Britt.
syn. *Lippia citriodora* H., B. et K.

Description: A small shrub up to 3 m high, with long, coarse branches. Leaves on short petioles, 50−80 mm long, glabrous, on the reverse numerous glandules visible as dots. When rubbed between the fingers the whole plant smells of lemons. Flowers small, white, with densely tomentose calyx, arranged in long panicles.

Origin and Distribution: Indigenous to Argentina and Chile. Cultivated for its fine-smelling volatile oil in France, Spain, Italy, the former USSR, and elsewhere.

Harvesting and Preparation: Propagated by seeds or cuttings; flowers usually twice a year, in summer and autumn. At the beginning of the flowering period the whole overground part of the plant is harvested.

Constituents: The leaves contain volatile oil, the so-called verbena (vervain) oil (0.2−0.3 per cent), which is obtained by distillation with steam or by extraction with volatile solvents. The best volatile oil comes from the varieties bred and cultivated in southern France; it contains mainly citral (up to 70 per cent), and also l-limonene, myrcene and geraniol. The volatile oil of Spanish origin contains mainly l-limonene, and also citral, verbenon.

Cosmetic Uses: Verbena oil is used in perfumery. It has a fresh, lemony scent and is used for perfuming soaps, lipsticks, hair oils, brilliantines, etc. It is also an ingredient in many perfumes. Being very rare and expensive, it is often replaced or mixed with the cheaper lemon-grass oil, called in this instance East Indian 'verbene' oil.

Other Uses: The related species, *Lippia adoensis* from western Africa and *Lippia pseudo-thea* from South America, are used for the preparation of tea, but are of local significance only. Some other species are used therapeutically.

Marshmallow

Malvaceae

Althaea officinalis L.

Description: A perennial plant up to 150 cm high, with whitish to light brown roots. The whole overground part of the plant is covered in soft hairs. Leaves on short petioles, irregularly dentate, the lower ones trilobate to pentalobate, the upper ones cordiform incised. Flowers white or pinkish, approximately 4 cm across, flowering from July to September. The flowers grow from the upper part of the stem, in loose racemes. Corolla of five petals, numerous stamens with deep violet to purple anthers.

Origin and Distribution: Indigenous to the eastern Mediterranean region. In Europe either cultivated or growing wild in warmer areas especially on the banks of streams, in humid meadows, thickets and pastureland.

Harvesting and Preparation: Leaves, flowers and roots, usually of the cultivated plants only, are gathered. The leaves and flowers are dried immediately after harvesting, in shade, as quickly as possible, at temperatures up to 50° C. The flowers must remain pinkish; incorrectly dried flowers are rusty red. Peeled and cut roots are dried at temperatures up to 40° C, also in shade. Correctly dried roots are light yellow; at higher temperatures they become somewhat darker.

Constituents: The main pharmacologically active components are mucilages; about 10 per cent of them are contained in the roots; the leaves and flowers contain somewhat smaller quantities. Their chemical composition is little known, yet they are known to contain lecithin, various amino acids and sugar components. Besides mucilages, traces of a volatile oil (0.02 per cent) and organic acids are found in the leaves and flowers. Mucilages help to prevent irritation of injured and healing tissues, as they form a thin protective film over the affected place and absorb skin secretions.

Cosmetic Uses: Marshmallow is commonly used in infusions for washing the skin, as an ingredient of cooling herbal face packs and in creams and emulsions. For the preparation of packs and infusions containing mucilaginous herbs, only lukewarm water should be used, as the mucilages form solid deposits in hot water. Marshmallow decoctions (100 g to a litre of lukewarm water, extracted for about an hour) can be added into moderately warm soothing baths for treating eczema.

Other Uses: In medicine marshmallow is used in the form of a tea for chronic inflammations of the respiratory tract and disturbed digestion in children.

Alkanet
Boraginaceae

Anchusa officinalis L.

Description: A biennial to triennial, rarely perennial plant, with a black, nearly unbranched root. From the root rise several stems forming short branches in the upper part. Stems 30–80 cm high, covered with rough hairs. Basal leaves in the first year are up to 20 cm long, narrowing into a petiole; during the flowering period they are already dry, and only the lanceolate shorter stem leaves, sessile at their cordiform base, remain on the plant. Flowers relatively small, with tubular corolla, first crimson-red, later deep violet-blue. Flowers arranged in short, dense coils, flowering from May to September.

Origin and Distribution: Native to eastern and central Europe, and introduced to the West. Fairly abundant on dry hillsides, pastureland and other sunny places on high and low ground.

Harvesting and Preparation: The whole herb is gathered during the flowering period and dried in shade.

Constituents: The flowering herb contains the following alkaloids: cynoglossin, consolidin, consolicin, tannins (up to 9 per cent), and numerous minor and little-known substances such as saccharides, a dye, organic acids, mucilages and mineral salts.

Cosmetic Uses: Although alkanet is little used today, either in commercial or folk medicine, it remains quite popular for beauty care. The pulped fresh herb can be used in the form of a herb pack to cool and soothe sensitive or irritated skin. The pulp can also be applied to painful, swollen areas and all types of insect bite, as it relieves the pain, reduces swelling and stops itching. Baths with the addition of an alkanet decoction (200 g per litre of hot water, extracted for 20 minutes) are recommended for soothing irritated skin, in eczema and for opening dirt-clogged pores.

Other Uses: Alkanet contains nectar, but a related species, *Anchusa italica* Retz., especially in its cultivated forms, contains more and is more widely used for this purpose.

Greater Burdock

Compositae

Arctium lappa L.

Description: A biennial plant with a massive, spindle-shaped root and branched stem up to 1 m high. During its first year it forms a leaf rosette, in its second year an erect, grooved, profusely and horizontally branched flower-bearing stem. Leaves are alternate, ovoid to slightly cordiform, grey and downy on the reverse. Flowers arranged in terminal cymose panicles; bracts around the flowers are red to slightly violet, with hooked spiny hairs. The fruit is an achene. Flowering time from July to August.

Distribution: The plant grows in Europe, Asia, Africa and America, usually along roadsides and on waste ground. Likes rich loamy soil, especially with a sand and limestone substratum.

Harvesting and Preparation: Roots of non-flowering, one-year-old plants are gathered in autumn, those of two-year-old plants in early spring. The roots of flowering plants are woody, and sometimes hollow. After digging out the roots they must be thoroughly washed and the thicker ones cut lengthwise, and dried at temperatures up to 50° C. Occasionally the leaves and fruit are gathered.

Constituents: Burdock root contains chemically unstable polyacetylene substances with antibacterial and fungicidal properties. It also contains triterpenoid glycosides. The leaves contain the germacranolid arctiopicrin and other, chemically unstable and little-known substances; they also contain mucilages, organic acids and mineral salts.

Cosmetic Uses: Either infusions or decoctions can be prepared from burdock, but because of the unstable nature of its active substances infusion is preferable. 20 g of the dried ground root or leaves to 1/4 l warm water are extracted and then filtered through a dense sieve. May be used as a hair rinse for excessive hair loss and dandruff or for washing the face in cases of acne and greasy skin. Effective against fungal diseases of the skin, such as athlete's foot, as a bath ingredient (1:5). The grated fresh root, applied as a face pack, is an excellent skin cleanser.

Other Uses: Important medicinally, mainly for diabetics as a component of teas regulating digestion and excretion.

Horseradish

Cruciferae

Armoracia rusticana Gaertn., Mey. et Scherb.

Description: A perennial plant about 40−100 cm high. It has a long, thick, cylindrical, fleshy root, light yellow on the surface, inside white, horizontally branching. Stem is leafy, erect, angular, glabrous, branched in its upper part. Basal leaves are large, on long petioles, forming a rosette. Flowers are small, white, with a pungent smell.

Origin and Distribution: Horseradish comes from southeastern Europe but it is now distributed throughout the whole of Europe. It is often cultivated in gardens but it spreads easily and can be found growing wild on the banks of streams, ponds and in other damp places.

Cultivation and Harvesting: Horseradish is cultivated for its fleshy roots. It requires deep, fertile, moist but well-drained soil. Its cultivation is relatively easy: it is propagated by root cuttings 20−30 cm long and about one finger thick, planted in spring. Harvest after 2−3 years in late autumn. Not suitable for drying. Use fresh, or store in sand in a cold cellar, for use as required.

Constituents: The root contains about 0.05 per cent volatile oil, vitamin C and little-known substances with a disinfectant effect. Horseradish oil belongs to the so-called mustard oils, releasing a pungent isothiocyanate with organically bound sulphur. Volatile oils of similar composition are contained in other cruciferous plants such as mustard (*Brassica nigra* (L.) Koch) and nasturtium (*Tropaeolum majus* L.), and also in garlic and onion.

Cosmetic Uses: Horseradish juice has regenerative, cleansing and disinfectant effects on greasy, blemished skin. However, prolonged use on the skin or too high a concentration may cause blisters, inflammation and swellings caused by irritation. May be used in a bath to promote blood circulation.

Other Uses: In medicine it is used externally for rheumatic diseases and sciatica, and internally against cold and coughs. Also used in cooking, as a condiment. Because of its sharp, hot taste it is good served with boiled and smoked meats, fish and added to mixed pickles.

Mountain Arnica

Arnica montana L.

Compositae

Description: A perennial plant with a horizontal, almost cylindrical root and ovoid leaves arranged in a rosette. Stem leaves are opposite, lanceolate. Stem erect, with glandular hairs, up to 50 cm high, simple or branched. Flowers large, orange-yellow, daisy-like, flowering from June to August. Fruit is an achene with light yellow downy tuft. The whole plant has a pleasant, spicy smell.

Distribution: Throughout Europe and North America. Prefers pastureland and non-chalky mountain meadows, but also occurs on lowland marshy grounds. Disappears from fertilized and intensively cultivated meadows.

Harvesting and Preparation: Arnica can be cultivated in suitable conditions. Flowers or the whole herb are dried in shade at 40° C. Washed rootstocks are dried in the sun or at artificial temperatures up to 70° C. The most valuable part are the florets. Less often used are the whole flower, the flowering herb or the rootstock.

Constituents: The drug has excellent healing effects, but it is not known which substances are responsible for them. Arnica contains 0.1 per cent volatile oil containing thymol and thymol ether in the florets. Further components are alcohols (arnidiol and faradiol), flavone glycosides, carotenoid pigments, etc. The constituents in the stems, leaves and rootstock have a different composition from those in the florets.

Cosmetic Uses: The non-irritant extract is used in anti-inflammatory and regenerative creams and in hair cosmetics. Arnica extract can also be used in cleansing creams, skin lotions and as an ingredient in facial steams before the application of face packs.

Other Uses: Arnica tincture (alcohol extract) is used externally on wounds to help them heal. Arnica was once extensively used for this purpose, and almost completely disappeared because of over-harvesting. The plant is toxic when used internally: 70 cc of the tincture represents a lethal dose for humans.

Southernwood

Compositae

Artemisia abrotanum L.

Description: A perennial subshrub with densely branched stems rising from one root. It reaches about 60 cm in height. Leaves hair-like, double pinnate, with filiform and linear leaf segments, smooth above, grey and downy on the reverse. Circular yellow flower heads resembling small discs are composed of tubular florets. Flowers from July to August. The plant has a very pleasant smell somewhat resembling lemons.

Origin and Distribution: Probably native to the Near East and southern Europe, but grows in Europe, Asia and Africa. Very popular in ancient times, and long cultivated in gardens for its strong fragrance. Rarely found in the wild. Grows best in high altitudes in full sun. Tolerates poor dry soils.

Harvesting and Preparation: Propagated by dividing old tufts or from seeds. The whole herb is harvested before flowering by cutting off the stem about 10 cm above the ground. It must be dried in shade to prevent loss of colour.

Constituents: The drug contains volatile oil (0.5 per cent) with thuione and thuiole, and the bitter substances artabasine and absinthin from which chamazulene, a substance effective against inflammations, is formed during distillation. Chamazulene is also found in chamomile and yarrow.

Cosmetic Uses: Southernwood is recommended either alone or in a mixture as an ingredient of invigorating baths. It improves blood circulation in the skin and has an anti-inflammatory and probably also disinfectant effect, mainly against fungal diseases. About 2 l boiling water poured over 500 g of southernwood and extracted for 30 minutes is added to the bath water. The bath should not be taken more than twice a week.

Other Uses: The *Artemisia* (mugwort) genus, comprising many species, has been used in medicine and as spice since ancient times. The bitter 'mugwort' taste and its favourable effect on digestion were known in ancient Egypt. The great medieval herbalist, Abbess Hildegard, mentions *'wermude'* (mugwort) as one of the most potent medicinal plants.

Oat

Gramineae

Avena sativa L.

Description: A grass cultivated since ancient times, with a loose panicle and kernels covered with husks. The massive root system supplies the plant with the considerable amounts of water it requires. It is resistant to cold and this is why it is a common crop plant of both temperate and cool climates. Usually sown in spring, sometimes in autumn.

Origin and Distribution: The oldest evidence of oats being used by man has been found in Swiss pile dwellings of the Bronze Age, but only in the early Middle Ages were they frequently cultivated, as evidence from Slavonic and German dwellings has shown. Nowadays oats are grown mainly in central and northern Europe, North America and to some extent in Australia.

Constituents: The kernels contain starch, proteins, traces of fat, and minerals such as iron, calcium, magnesium and phosphorus. The outer layers of the kernels contain the vitamins B_1, B_2 and B_{12}. The husks contain the glycoside vanillosid, which acts as a stimulant on oat-fed horses.

Cosmetic Uses: Ground, unhulled kernels or oat flakes may be added to the bath for exhaustion and for calming irritation. About 1 kg of oat flakes in a cloth bag are added to a hot bath and extracted until the bath becomes lukewarm. The bath should last 20−30 minutes. Oat bran is useful for washing very sensitive skin and for the preparation of face packs, (as is almond bran). It should be mixed with boiled water to form a stiff paste which is then applied to the face and washed off after 10 minutes with lukewarm water. To lighten dark skin make a paste from a mixture of 25 g oat flour, 25 g rice flour and 100 g almond bran, diluted with a decoction of lime flowers, and use as a face pack.

Other Uses: Oat is important both in the human diet and also as a fodder crop. From the kernels, oat flakes *(Flocci avenae)* or groats *(Glarea avenae)* are made. According to the Swiss physician Dr Bircher-Benner oat flakes soaked in water for 12 hours and then mixed with honey, lemon juice, yoghurt and various kinds of fruit to make meusli, and eaten regularly, will improve one's physical and mental health, make the hair glossy and elastic and the skin smooth and fine.

Silver Birch

Betulaceae

Betula pendula Roth

Description: A slender, fast-growing tree with white bark that peels off in paper-thin layers. It grows to a height of up to 18 m, and has pendulous, red-brown branches with resin-bearing surface cells. Leaves are triangular-ovoid, on long stalks. Young leaves are light green and discharge a sticky secretion; later the leaves get darker. Male and female flowers are borne in cylindrical catkins, developing into seed cones.

Distribution: Birch will grow in any soil and is extraordinarily resistant to cold. It is distributed throughout Europe, Canada and northern USA, growing in lowlands as well as on high ground. Silver birch has many varieties which are grown in gardens.

Harvesting and Preparation: Young leaves are gathered from spring to summer, when they contain the greatest quantity of active substances. Should be dried in natural conditions in shade, or artificially at temperatures up to 40° C. The plant has a pleasant aromatic smell and a slightly bitter taste.

Active Substances: Mainly saponins, but also flavone compounds, carotenoids, vitamin C and volatile oils with disinfectant, anti-rheumatic and diuretic effects.

Cosmetic Uses: The disinfectant effects of birch are made use of in bath additives. A decoction (100 g per litre of boiling water, extracted for 20 minutes) cleanses the skin surface and unclogs the pores. Its vitamin C content aids the regenerative capacity of the skin. 'Birch water' made with spring birch sap flowing out from bored trunks, is used as a hair tonic. The sap, rich in sugar components and organic acids, is preserved to avoid fermentation and then added to ethanol. The resulting birch water clears dandruff, removes grease and improves the elasticity and appearance of the hair.

Other Uses: Birch tar *(Oleum betulinum)* was once used in dermatology for suppurating rashes; the tar was obtained by dry distillation of birch wood. Nowadays it is not much used in medicine, mainly because of its penetrating, unpleasant smell.

Borage
Boraginaceae

Borago officinalis L.

Description: A robust annual plant, up to 60 cm high. Stem hollow, simple or branched, covered with bristly hairs. Leaves elliptical, wrinkled, rough, the lower ones on short petioles, the upper ones sessile. Flowers, on long stalks, are about 2 cm in diameter with a calyx of five sepals and a 5-pointed corolla, usually blue, sometimes white. Flowers from June till September. Fruit ovoid, light brown.

Origin and Distribution: Origin uncertain, thought to be southern Europe. Easily propagated by seed and naturalized in many places.

Harvesting and Preparation: The herb is gathered at the beginning of the flowering period and dried in shade or quickly in the sun. The drug smells and tastes of cucumbers.

Constituents: Remarkably rich in mucilages; contains a small quantity of saponins and tannins; relatively rich in mineral salts and vitamin C.

Cosmetic Uses: Borage can be used in the same way as cucumber. As the fresh herb is very rich in sap, it yields a lot of juice which is excellent for skin cleansing, for removing impurities from clogged pores and for closing the pores. Borage is therefore very useful in home beauty care. The plant may be pulped or squeezed to extract the juice. Cotton wool soaked in the juice and applied as a face pack tightens, refines and cools the skin, and narrows the capillaries thus reducing reddening of the skin. For sensitive skin, pure juice and not the whole pulp is recommended; the pulp usually contains hairs from the stem and leaves which may irritate sensitive skin.

Other Uses: In folk medicine borage is used as a diuretic, removing harmful substances from the body. Young leaves are used in salads and are added to pickles, bean soup and fruit and wine cups, for a cucumber flavour.

Marigold

Compositae

Calendula officinalis L.

Description: An annual plant with an erect, branched stem 40−50 cm high. Leaves are sessile and hairy. Large, orange-yellow terminal flower-heads appear from June till autumn. Cultivated plants often flower profusely. Fruits are small, ridged or crescent-like involuted achenes, spiky on the dorsal side.

Origin and Distribution: Native to the Mediterranean region, and cultivated throughout Europe. Only rarely found wild. Grows in all moist soils, but requires full sun. It is propagated from seed.

Harvesting and Preparation: For cosmetic and pharmaceutical purposes either the whole flower-head or just the ray florets are gathered. They should be harvested in dry weather and dried in shade. When dried in the sun they lose colour and depreciate. The drug easily absorbs moisture.

Constituents: The pharmacologically active substances are yellow and red carotenoid pigments which are soluble in fat, traces of volatile oil (approximately 0.02 per cent) and organic acids, particularly salicylic acid. The complex of active substances has a disinfectant, anti-inflammatory effect and heals damaged tissue.

Cosmetic Uses: The flowers or their oil extract are used in healing creams for chapped hands and healed, but still sore, burns and chilblains. Medicated oils and emulsions are also manufactured for these purposes. To prepare marigold oil at home, pack the flower-heads tightly into broad-necked glass jars, screw on the lids and place on a sunny window-sill. After several days an oily orange fluid will be produced and will form a sediment on the bottom of the jars. Marigold oil is used in the same way as marigold ointment, to clear and soften the skin and soothe irritation.

Other Uses: Marigold is used in medicine not only on the skin but also internally in the form of an infusion for the complexion, indigestion and gall bladder disorders.

Chinese Tea

Theaceae

Camellia sinensis (L.) O. Kuntze

Description: A subtropical evergreen shrub up to 3 m high, with numerous coppice shoots by which the plant naturally rejuvenates itself. Leathery leaves are deep green and slightly serrated. Pedicellate flowers are whitish to yellowish, with 5 petals and numerous (about 200) stamens with bright yellow anthers and trifid stigma. Fruit is a brown, leathery capsule containing large oily seeds.

Origin and Distribution: Central and southeastern China is the homeland of Chinese tea — more aromatic but less productive than Indian tea which is indigenous to the Sub-Himalayan region. Other tea brands are only commercial designations.

Harvesting and Preparation: Tea is grown in plantations in the whole subtropical zone, and harvested several times a year. Young offshoots, the so-called 'flashes', are gathered; from them either fermented, black tea, popular in Europe, semi-fermented (oolong) tea, or unfermented, green tea, drunk in China and southeastern Asia, is obtained. Approximately 4,500 'flashes' must be picked to obtain 1 kg of dried tea.

Constituents: Both kinds of tea contain the stimulating and invigorating alkaloid caffeine, a small amount of theophylline, theobromine and tannins. The amount of these substances varies considerably, not so much according to brand as according to the position of the leaves on the twig. The young, undeveloped leaves on the tips of the plant contain the highest quantities of caffeine and tannins; the quantities decrease the further down the plant the leaves are.

Cosmetic Uses: For cosmetic purposes, the tannin content in tea makes an infusion useful for closing the pores and as a general skin tonic to improve the appearance of the skin. Tea also has a soothing and disinfectant effect. Tea may be used for washing off a face pack (do not use soap for this). A resinoid extracted from tea of quality too poor to drink is used in some perfumes for men, as its scent resembles that of tobacco.

Other Uses: Tea is an important crop, harvested for the preparation of a refreshing beverage, popular throughout most of the world.

Ylang-ylang

Annonaceae

Cananga odorata (Lam.) Hook f. ex Thoms.

Description: An evergreen tropical tree, about 8−12 m high. Leaves are ellipsoid, 7−20 cm long. Yellow flowers, with lingulate petals approximately 7 cm long, usually form clusters on older wood. Fruit is similar to olives; ripe fruit is black, containing several flat seeds.

Origin and Distribution: Originally grew wild only in Malaysia; now cultivated in numerous tropical countries. The main producers of the cananga volatile oils were the Philippines, later Java. At present Reunion has a production monopoly.

Cultivation and Harvesting: Grown as an ornamental tree, mainly for its strongly fragrant flowers which are the source of a rare volatile oil. Cultivated trees begin to flower 18 months to 2 years after planting. In order to facilitate flower picking the trees are cut down to about 3 m high. A four-year-old plant yields about 4−5 kg flowers annually, the yield of a 10-year-old plants being 10−12 kg. The flowers are gathered early in the morning when the content of the volatile oil is the highest.

Constituents: The volatile oil (1.5−2.5 per cent) is distilled from the flowers with steam. It has a very pleasant flowery smell, and is amber-yellow in colour. The volatile oil contains over 20 substances, the most important of which are linalool, geraniol and eugenol.

Cosmetic Uses: The volatile oil of ylang-ylang is highly prized in perfumery. It is used in deodorant sprays, and also forms part of perfumes such as lavender, jasmine, rose, Fougère, Chanel No 5 and others.

Other Uses: In Indonesia cananga flowers are used in native ritual dances and for the preparation of fragrant herbal beverages.

Safflower

Carthamus tinctorius L.

Compositae

Description: An annual plant with erect, branched, smooth stems becoming woody during the ripening period. Reaches a height of 100–150 cm, according to the variety and habitat. Leaves are mostly oblong-lanceolate, dentate to serrate. Orange tubular florets form flower-heads about 1.5 to 3 cm in diameter. Fruit is an oblong glossy achene with 4 slightly prominent ribs on the surface. Each achene contains one oily seed.

Origin and Distribution: A very old cultivated plant, native to eastern India. It was known in ancient Egypt, Greece and Rome. Today it occurs most abundantly in central Asia, India and the Mediterranean region. Cultivated in Europe and the USA.

Constituents: The seeds contain a desiccating oil (20 per cent) formed from 75 per cent by linoleic acid. It can be processed to make an edible oil. The flowers contain a dark red colouring substance called carthamin.

Cosmetic Uses: Mainly of historic importance in cosmetics. Carthamin was used as a dye in ancient Egypt in the preparation of grease paints, and is used today in some theatre grease paints. The desiccating oil cannot be used, as it often irritates sensitive skin (as do sunflower, walnut, linseed and hempseed oils) and is therefore unsuitable for cosmetic purposes.

Other Uses: Carthamin has been used since 2000 BC for the preparation of dyes and the dyeing of cloth. Since the 18th century the importance of safflower as an oil-bearing plant has increased, and it is cultivated today mainly for the oil content in its seeds, which is refined to make an edible oil.

Common Chamomile

Compositae

Chamaemelum nobile (L.) All.
syn. *Anthemis nobilis* L.

Description: A low perennial plant up to 30 cm high. Stem's main axis is prominent, procumbent, with numerous offshoots. Leaves are double pinnate, finely dissected. Disc-shaped flower-heads with white ray florets, yellow tubular central disc florets. Unlike wild chamomile whose ray florets bend back, those of common chamomile are prominent.

Origin and Distribution: Grows wild in Europe, especially in its native Mediterranean region. In some countries it is cultivated as field culture. Likes sunny habitats and light soils rich in humus. It is propagated only vegetatively, by means of seedlings obtained by division of established plants.

Harvesting and Preparation: Flower-heads should be harvested at noon between June and August, in dry weather, and dried as quickly as possible at approximately 30° C. Dried flowers absorb moisture easily and turn brown, so they should be kept in airtight containers. Volatile oil is obtained from the flower-heads by distillation (1−1.5 per cent).

Constituents: The main active substance of the volatile oil, distilled for the first time in Frankfurt in the 16th century, is chamazulene, as in wild chamomile. Besides the volatile oil, the plant contains flavone glycosides, bitter substances and organic acids. These have anti-inflammatory, disinfectant and anti-spasmodic effects.

Cosmetic Uses: The volatile oil is added to face lotions, soaps and bath additives. It has the same properties and effects as wild chamomile, which is more commonly available in shops. A lukewarm infusion (10 g per 100 cc boiling water, extracted for 15 minutes) may be used for washing sores, boils and inflamed skin and as a rinse for greasy hair and dandruff. In face packs common chamomile can replace wild chamomile.

Both herbs can cause an allergic swelling or rash in sensitive skin, in which case preparations containing them must not be used.

Other Uses: Medicinally, common chamomile is used internally in the form of an infusion for indigestion and stomach cramps, and for difficult menstruation. It is used externally in dermatology and for diseases of the mouth.

Wild Chamomile

Compositae

Chamomilla recutita (L.) Rauschert
syn. *Matricaria chamomilla* L.

Description: An annual plant with a thin, spindle-shaped root and erect, branched stem. When cultivated, it can reach more than 50 cm in height. Leaves finely dissected, sessile. Terminal flower-heads have white peripheral ray florets and yellow tubular disc florets. Receptacles are hollow, unlike those of other related species. In Europe it flowers from May till September.

Distribution: Common in Europe, Asia, North America and Australia. Grows wild, but extensively cultivated in field cultures. Prefers sunny habitats.

Harvesting and Preparation: Flower-heads should be harvested in the afternoon, by hand or by means of combs and dried quickly, in thin layers, in shade.

Constituents: The most important active substance is the fragrant volatile oil which contains chamazulene and bisabol. Chamazulene gives the oil its blue colour and has pronounced anti-inflammatory and healing effects.

Cosmetic Uses: Extracts as well as the pure volatile oil are used in nearly all types of cosmetic — creams, soaps, face lotions, packs, bath oils, shampoos and conditioners, etc. — for their beneficial, soothing effect on the skin, and their healing, cleansing and regenerative properties. The herb is used in face packs and for washing before and after applying the pack. Hair rinses of chamomile infusion brighten dark hair and intensify the colour of fair hair, and improve its elasticity and gloss. A chamomile infusion added to the bath helps to cleanse the skin, and is especially useful as an aid to recovery after rashes, ulcers, etc. The infusion is prepared by pouring 100 cc boiling water over 10 g of the herb and extracting it for about 10 minutes. It is then added to the bath water.

Other Uses: Chamomile is an invaluable medicinal plant, especially for children. It is used internally for treating colic, insomnia and nervous conditions. There is no other drug with such a broad use in folk medicine.

Carrageen, Irish Moss

Gigartinaceae

Chondrus crispus (L.) Stackhouse

Description: A seaweed in the form of a multicellular, leaf-like, branched thallus of ribbon-like fronds sub-divided at their ends. The shape of the thallus is variable. The green colouring substance chlorophyll is covered with the red pigment phycoerythrine which gives the alga its crimson to purple colour. The thallus turns green in strong sunlight, however.

Distribution: Grows on coastal rocks in the northern parts of the Atlantic ocean, abundantly in some places, particularly Ireland (hence the name), but the main supplier is the USA.

Harvesting and Preparation: The seaweed is raked from the water and spread out in the sun to be dried and bleached. The procedure is repeated 4−5 times, until the seaweed becomes pale yellow and elastic in texture.

Constituents: Cosmetically and medicinally, algae such as carrageen and agar-agar form a separate group of plants yielding special drugs. Carrageen contains 45 per cent mucilages called carragenins, consisting of about 28 per cent sulphates. It also contains small quantities of iodine and bromine.

Cosmetic Uses: The physical properties of carrageen (especially its swelling capacity, due to its high content of sticky, gelatinous and mucilaginous substances) are used in the manufacture of face creams, and to make gels and emulsions for the preparation of fat-free ointment bases. Marine algae are said to have beneficial effects on dry and ageing skin. Because of its laxative effect carrageen is added to slimming teas. Agar-agar, obtained from red algae, as well as other alginates from brown algae, are used cosmetically in a similar way to carrageen.

Other Uses: Carrageen is used therapeutically in infusions and decoctions for coughs, bronchitis, gastric ulcers and as a mild laxative. Its main role, however, is in the pharmaceutical industry, in the preparation of gels and emulsions. Also added to tablets to help them breakdown easily.

Tansy

Compositae

Chrysanthemum vulgare (L.) Bernh.
syn. *Tanacetum vulgare* L.

Description: A perennial plant with branched, almost woody, brown rootstock. Stem erect, angular, up to 160 cm high, terminating in a branched panicle. Leaves are oblong-ovoid, pinnately divided, with toothed segments. Small yellow flowers, about 10 mm across, flower from July to September. Individual florets ripen to small achenes.

Distribution: Common in Europe, the USA and Asia. Abundant on waste ground and along streams, ridges and roadsides.

Harvesting and Preparation: The flowering herb is gathered in dry weather and dried quickly in shade. Artificial temperature must not exceed 40° C. The herb has a camphor-like smell and bitter, spicy taste. The smell of dried tansy repels insects.

Constituents: The whole herb, especially the flowers, contains a poisonous volatile oil. It also contains thujone (up to 65 per cent), 1-camphor, borneol, thujyalcohol, bitter substances and tanacetins.

Cosmetic Uses: Tansy is little used in cosmetics since it can be poisonous. It may be used in stimulating baths and insect repellents (in the form of sprays or creams). Repellents, though not strictly cosmetics, can be included here because, by repelling insects, they prevent the formation of the swellings and scars caused by insect bites. Repellents often contain other volatile oils such as cinnamon, mint, clove and lime. They are added either to rich, oily liniments or sprays. The disadvantage of these preparations is that they irritate the skin and cause allergies.

Use only under medical supervision.

Other Uses: In the USA tansy oil is used in veterinary medicine against intestinal parasites of cattle. Due to its toxicity the volatile oil is little used in human medicine.

Cassia Bark Tree

Lauraceae

Cinnamomum aromaticum Nees
syn. *Cinnamomum cassia* Blume

Description: An evergreen tropical tree up to 12 m high. The trunk has cracked, ash-grey bark; leathery leaves are light green, aromatic, with distinct venation. Flowers are tiny, inconspicuous, arranged in clusters, exuding a pleasant smell. Resembles the cinnamon to which it is closely related.

Origin and Distribution: Indigenous to southern China. Cultivated mainly in China, Thailand and Indonesia.

Processing and Preparation: The bark of the cassia bark tree, the so-called cassia *(Cortex cinnamomi chinensis),* forms simple yellow-brown tubes or semicircular or flat strips. The Ceylon cinnamon, which is of higher quality and value, is processed in involuted double tubes.

Constituents: According to place of origin, the content and chemical composition of the volatile oil (called cinnamon oil), the most important constituent of the bark, differs. Cassia: 1−2 per cent volatile oil with 75−90 per cent cinnamon aldehyde, without eugenol; Ceylon cinnamon: 1−1.5 per cent volatile oil with 65−75 per cent aldehyde and 10 per cent eugenol. Burmese and Seychelles cinnamons have other components as well. Besides volatile oil cassia (cinnamon) contains a small quantity of mucilage and tannins.

Cosmetic Uses: Cassia (cinnamon) oil is used cosmetically either distilled from the bark or distilled from the leaves. It has strong disinfectant and deodorising effects which is why it is added to toothpastes, mouthwashes and mouth sprays. Cassia (cinnamon) aldehyde is used in perfume manufacture. As the natural volatile oil is rather expensive, it is usually manufactured synthetically.

Other Uses: The bark of all cultivated varieties of cinnamon is important as a spice, used either ground or whole. Because of its flavour it is very popular in the food industry and in the manufacture of liqueurs.

Camphor Tree

Lauraceae

Cinnamomum camphora (L.) J. S. Presl

Description: A tropical branching tree up to 12 m high. Evergreen, leathery leaves are ovoid, acuminate, on long petioles. Tiny greenish-yellow flowers arranged in axillary panicles on long pedicels. Fruit are dark red, pea-sized berries.

Origin and Distribution: Native to Taiwan, China and Japan, and successfully cultivated in Sri Lanka, Madagascar and Florida, as it grows well in all warm regions.

Cultivation and Harvesting: Best propagated from seed, but can also be grown from root or stem cuttings. In plantations it is maintained in shrub form, growing up to 2.5 m height. Harvesting can be started 3–4 years after planting, and is done by cutting off the twigs successively. All parts of the plant contain camphor oil. When the plantation is 50–60 years old, the trees are cut down and the wood is ground into small pieces which are then distilled with steam. From 20–40 kg of wood about 2 kg of volatile oil are obtained, from which 1 kg of camphor is extracted.

Constituents: All parts of the tree, including the roots, contain cells in which the volatile oil is concentrated; its main component, besides safrol, eugenol and cineol, is camphor. At room temperature camphor forms a solid, crystalline substance. The volatile oil from the roots contains less camphor but more safrol. The content of volatile oil in the leaves varies from 10–75 per cent according to the plant's place of origin and its age.

Cosmetic Uses: Camphor is an outstanding means of improving blood circulation and it also has cooling and disinfectant effects. For these reasons it is contained in most massage creams, refreshing skin creams and face lotions. In perfumery the volatile oil Ho-oil (Shin-oil), containing linalool with a fine camphor odour, is used.

Other Uses: In pharmacy camphor is used in various anti-neuralgic and anti-rheumatic ointments and is also sometimes used internally in oil injections for regulating heart activity and blood circulation.

Lime

Rutaceae

Citrus aurantiifolia (Christm.) Swingle

Description: An evergreen subtropical or tropical tree up to 5−6 m high. It has irregular short branches with very sharp thorns. Its light green leaves are oval or elliptical, 5−7 cm long, with a narrow winged petiole. Yellowish-white flowers, 15−25 mm in size, grow from the leaf axils in groups of two to seven. In the tropics it flowers practically all year round. Fruits are broadly oval to globose berries, 35−50 mm in diameter, greenish-yellow to brown-yellow. The pulp is usually divided into 10−12 segments containing spindle-shaped vesicles with a sour-tasting juice like lemon juice but more acid.

Origin and Distribution: Probably comes from the region comprising north-eastern India, part of Burma and northern Malaysia from where its cultivation spread, with Spanish and Portuguese navigators in the 16th century, to the Mediterranean region and to the western hemisphere. Nowadays cultivated, in the same way as other citruses, in plantations, for its fruit.

Constituents: The fruit, limes, contain in their green pulp juice citric and other organic acids, sugars and vitamins C and B.

From the rind of the immature fruit the volatile oil (1 per cent) akin to lemon oil, is expressed. It contains citral, bisabolone, bergaptene and other components.

Cosmetic Uses: Lime has limited uses cosmetically: only in perfumery is lime oil used, as is lemon oil, in perfume blends. Its advantage over lemon oil is that it keeps twice as long, but because its production is considerably lower its significance is negligible.

Other Uses: Limes may be used instead of lemons in the preparation of sauces, jams, syrups and pectins; lime juice is used to make soft drinks and in the manufacture of citric acid.

74

Seville Orange
Rutaceae

Citrus aurantium L. ssp. *aurantium*

Description: An evergreen subtropical citrus tree resembling the sweet orange tree, 4–5 m high. Leaves are broadly winged, oblong, glossy, with petioles and a strong smell when crushed. Flowers are pure white. Fruit is an orange, broadly oval berry with orange, somewhat bitter pulp.

Origin and Distribution: Native to eastern India and the adjacent parts of China and Burma. Because of the high resistance of its roots to rotting it is widely used as a rootstock for other citruses. Cultivated in plantations mainly around Seville in Spain; this is why it is often called the Seville orange (Bigarade orange, also known as the bitter, or sour, orange).

Cultivation and Harvesting: Forms with coloured foliage sometimes grown as ornamental plants. The leaves, flowers and orange rind are used for the manufacture of various types of volatile oils.

Constituents: From the leaves and offshoots volatile oil (0.3 per cent), known in perfumery as petitgrain oil *(Oleum petitgrain),* is distilled. The volatile oil is obtained from the flowers by distilling it with fat; this volatile oil is called neroli oil *(Oleum neroli* or *Oleum aurantiflorum).* Its quantity amounts to 0.1–0.5 per cent. Finally, volatile oils of other types are distilled in 0.7 and 1–2.5 per cent amounts from immature fruit and the rind of mature fruit. All these volatile oils contain the fragrant limonen and numerous other components in various ratios.

Cosmetic Uses: Volatile oils from the Seville orange form part of most well-known perfumes, including cologne (as one of the basic substances), Crêpe de Chine, gardenia and chypre (as one of the nuancers).

Other Uses: Because of their scent, all types of orange oil are used in the food industry for flavouring and aromatizing liquors and marmalades. This species is not eaten fresh but used to make a slightly bitter marmalade.

Bergamot

Rutaceae

Citrus aurantium ssp. *bergamia* Risso et Poit.

Description: A low, subtropical, evergreen tree; its leaves resemble those of the lemon tree, but the petioles are winged. No thorns. Flowers and flower buds are pure white on both sides. Unlike the lemon tree which flowers several times a year, bergamot flowers only once a year. Mature fruits are yellow, globose or broadly pyriform; in some cultivars (Terminello) the style remains on the fruit until ripe. Pulp is sour, with a pleasant scent.

Origin and Distribution: Native to southeastern Asia. The largest plantations are found around Calabria in Italy; also cultivated in the West Indies, India and Guinea.

Cultivation and Preparation: Cultivated for the pericarp of the immature fruit from which 0.4−0.6 per cent volatile oil is expressed. Volatile oil for perfume manufacture is also obtained from the leaves.

Constituents: The main components of the volatile oil are up to 40 per cent linalyl acetate, which gives the oil its characteristic scent, d-limonen, dipenten, citral, and bergaptene. The world annual production of bergamot oil is about 200,000 kg.

Cosmetic Uses: Its refreshing, pleasant scent makes it the most used of all citrus oils in perfumery. It is often used in cologne-type perfumes added to various cosmetics, particularly soaps. The terpenes have to be removed from the oil before it is used, as some people are allergic to them.

Lemon

Rutaceae

Citrus limon (L.) Burm. f.

Description: An evergreen subtropical tree, 3−6 m high, with a spherical, irregular crown. Branches are thick and usually thorny. Elliptical leaves have a short, unwinged petiole. Young leaves and flower buds are pink; older leaves are light green, and opened flowers are white. Fragrant flowers, 40−50 mm in diameter, growing individually or in sparse panicles in the leaf axils. Fruit is a berry, at each end narrowing into conical points, with light green to yellow rind. Rind is thick, not easy to peel, with a pleasant, fresh scent. Pulp usually consists of 8−10 segments containing vesicles with a sharp, sour, aromatic juice.

Origin and Distribution: Indigenous to the eastern Sub-Himalayan region, and now cultivated mainly in Sicily, Spain and California. Ripe fruit is harvested by cutting off the individual berries, as with other citruses.

Constituents: Lemons are a rich source of vitamin C. The rind contains 0.7−1.4 per cent volatile oil consisting prevailingly of limonen. Citral is the substance responsible for the characteristic scent of lemon oil. The juicy pulp contains organic acids, mainly citric acid (up to 7 per cent), sugars and vitamins C and B.

Cosmetic Uses: Both the juice and the oil are used. Lemon face packs are very popular, as they effectively cleanse the skin and close the pores. A good way of making one is to cut a lemon into pieces and put it in a jar with 30 per cent alcohol. Leave for a week in a dark place, then strain. To use, cotton wool is soaked with the liquid, applied to the face and left on for 15 minutes. Then the face is washed with lukewarm water. Lemon juice may be used in many other ways, in creams, skin cleansers and shampoos, in baths to whiten the skin and as a hair rinse for blonde hair. Lemon oil is extensively used in the perfume industry.

Other Uses: Its high vitamin C content makes lemon juice of nutritional value. It is widely used in the food industry to flavour food and drinks. Both the rind and juice are used in cooking, to make jams, syrups, sauces and puddings. Inferior lemons are processed to make citric acid.

Egyptian Myrrh

Burseraceae

Commiphora abyssinica (Berg.) Engl.

Description: A shrub or small tree adapted to extremely dry conditions. Branches thorny, covered with small stiff leaves. Flowers may be either hermaphrodite or unisexual. Fruit is a semipulpy drupe.

Distribution: Grows on the coast of eastern Africa, in Arabia, northern India and the Yemen.

Preparation: The plant exudes the golden-yellow resin called myrrh, which is obtained by making cuts into the stem and branches of wild or, rarely, cultivated plants; myrrh flows from the canals made in the bark and rapidly solidifies on contact with air to form hard, tear-shaped grains. Myrrh has been known in the Near East since ancient times and was brought, according to the Bible, as a gift to the newborn Christ by one of the Three Magi. Myrrh has lost its old importance in medicine and in embalming, but is still a significant raw material in some cosmetic and pharmaceutical preparations. The source of myrrh is not only *C. abyssinica;* the genus *Commiphora* comprises around 300 species, some of which, notably *C. africana* from Sudan and Ethiopia and *C. schimperi* from Ethiopia and western Arabia, also shed gum resin.

Constituents: Myrrh contains up to 10 per cent volatile oil consisting of many components including pinene, m-cresol, limonen and eugenol. It contains 30 per cent resins and 50−60 per cent gums. It is soluble in ethanol.

Cosmetic Uses: Myrrh is used in toothpastes and mouthwashes for its disinfectant and deodorant properties. The resinoid obtained from myrrh by distillation is used for perfuming soaps. The resinoid from the gum resin *C. chironium* is called opoponax and is one of the main perfumes used in modern cosmetics. It is used to perfume soaps, lipsticks, powders, mouthwashes and toothpastes, and is an excellent scent fixative.

Other Uses: Ethanolic solution of myrrh *(Tinctura myrrhae)* is used for the treatment of inflammations in the mouth.

Saffron

Iridaceae

Crocus sativus L.

Description: A perennial plant with a scaly underground bulb (corm) about the size of a walnut. Linear leaves with a white central nerve and a short flower-bearing stem grow from the corm in spring. The flower-stem terminates in a pale violet flower with six regular petals. The typical pistil has an inferior ovary and style branching out into three orange stigmas. The dried stigmas with a portion of the style are the parts used.

Origin and Distribution: Cultivated for centuries as a valuable spice, drug, perfume and dye. Saffron was mentioned as a remedy in an ancient Egyptian papyrus dating from 2 000 BC. It is probably native to Asia Minor, Iraq and Kashmir, but its cultivation had spread throughout the Orient, India and China a thousand years ago. It was brought to central and western Europe by the Crusaders in the 11th century.

Cultivation, Harvesting and Preparation: Growing saffron is extremely expensive and laborious. The bulbs are planted in August and the flowers are harvested for approximately 3 years, always in autumn, during the early morning. Then the stigmas with a part of the style are cut out and dried in the sun. For 1 kg dry saffron about 80,000 flowers are needed.

Constituents: The main component of saffron oil (0.4−1 per cent) is safranol which gives saffron its characteristic smell of iodine. The glycoside picrocrocin gives it its somewhat bitter taste. Saffron also contains carotenoid pigments and carotenes which make it useful as an orange-red dye.

Cosmetic Uses: Saffron is now considered obsolete in cosmetics, for although it is a highly efficient colouring agent, harmless to health, it can be easily replaced by the natural colouring substance from turmeric which is much cheaper to produce.

Other Uses: The significance of saffron in medicine is negligible today, as it is in the food industry, because of its high price and limited production. Today saffron is usually replaced by cheaper substitutes.

Cucumber

Cucurbitaceae

Cucumis sativus L.

Description: A tropical annual plant with an angular stem. Creeping or twining stems have tendrils and are usually 1−4 m long. Branched roots rarely penetrate deeper than 20−25 cm into the soil. Leaves are bright green, long petioled, rough, with five points. Flowers are bright yellow. Fruits are large, oblong, club-shaped, ovoid or cylindrical berries. Immature fruits are green, ripe ones orange-yellow to brown.

Origin and Distribution: Native to the northern part of eastern India. Cucumbers first appeared in Greece and Italy in about the 5th century BC, and their bitter-tasting fruit was consumed either fresh, or steamed or baked. The present cultivated cucumber came to Europe in the 17th century from Byzantium (now Turkey), and their cultivation spread throughout the temperate zone, being grown in fields, gardens and greenhouses.

Constituents: Cucumber juice contains organic acids, sugars, traces of chlorophyll, salt solutions, a vitamin complex and other substances, the so-called bioactivators with a pronounced diuretic and 'blood-cleansing' effect.

Cosmetic Uses: One of the best skin cleansers, suitable even for hypersensitive skin which cannot tolerate soap or hard water. Cucumber juice can be used fresh, or in the form of a skin lotion: fresh cucumbers are grated with a stainless-steel grater, mixed with an equal amount of diluted alcohol and extracted for about a week in a closed glass vessel. Then the resulting fluid is strained off and the rest pressed out from the pulp, and an equal amount of distilled water and 2 spoonfuls of glycerol are added. Face packs prepared from fresh grated cucumber are excellent for problem skin with clogged pores. A cucumber pack has an astringent, slightly whitening and smoothing effect on tired or rough skin. Ready-made cucumber extracts are used in many manufactured products.

Other Uses: Cucumbers are grown as a popular vegetable and are used mainly raw in salads. Large amounts are also preserved by pickling.

Turmeric

Zingiberaceae

Curcuma longa L.

Description: A tropical herbaceous plant growing from underground rhizomes and reaching 60–100 cm in height. The leaves are ellipsoid-oblong, the flowers yellow on flower-bearing stems.

Origin and Distribution: Imported from India to Europe by the Arabs in ancient times. Today it is cultivated mainly in China and India, and to a lesser extent in Java, Haiti, Japan, the Madagascar and the Philippines.

Harvesting and Preparation: The part of the plant used is the yellow rootstock. After harvesting, the rhizomes are cleaned, scalded with hot water and slowly dried in the sun. Parts of the main rhizome, each the size of a walnut, are sold under the name round curcuma, while pieces of the secondary rhizomes are called long curcuma. The best of the cultivated species is the Chinese turmeric, which is golden-yellow on the outside and orange or golden-yellow within.

Constituents: Turmeric contains 1.5 to 5.5 per cent volatile oil, the main components of which are turmeron (more than 50 per cent) and zingiberene (25 per cent), and also phellandrene, borneol and cineol. It also contains the yellow pigment curcumine, and starch.

Cosmetic Uses: In cosmetics turmeric is mainly used as a dye in lipsticks, skin foundations and hair tints. Turmeric has been used as a dye since the Middle Ages when, because of its colour, it was also known as Indian saffron. Turmeric oil is used to make oriental-type perfumes.

Other Uses: In the food industry dried turmeric is powdered and used as condiment, either alone or in mixtures (curry powder, mustard, Worcester sauce), to add flavour and colour. Often substituted for saffron. Javanese turmeric *(Rhizoma curcumae xanthorrhizae)* contains volatile oil with therapeutic effects on the gall-bladder and liver.

Quince
Cydonia oblonga Mill.

Rosaceae

Description: A small, deciduous tree 4−6 m high, with a spherical crown, twisted branches and dark bark. Leaves, on short petioles, are broadly oval, 50−100 mm long, smooth above and downy underneath. Showy, white or light pink flowers, 50−70 mm across, grow singly, usually at the ends of shoots, and the trees in blossom are very decorative. Fruit is a yellow, pleasant-smelling, acid-tasting, pear-shaped pome, about 70−100 mm long, with a downy surface.

Origin and Distribution: Native to southern Europe and Asia, and now cultivated throughout the temperate zone of the Old and New Worlds.

Cultivation: Self-fertile, but propagated by cuttings grafted onto quince, hawthorn or rowan rootstocks. Grown as a rootstock for some pear varieties. Cultivars include Angara, Champion, Portugal and Smyrna. Established tree regularly bears 15−20 kg fruit annually. The quince requires a warm habitat and does not tolerate chalky soil.

Constituents: The fruit contains organic acids, sugars and tannins. Quince fruit holds many seeds with an absorbent perisperm. Embryo contains 15 per cent oil, perisperm up to 22 per cent mucilage the larger part of which is soluble in cold water. The seeds must not be ground, as they contain poisonous amygdalin.

Cosmetic Uses: A mucilaginous infusion of the seeds (30 g seeds to 250 ml cold water, extracted for 2 to 3 hours) is used, often in skin creams, as a coolant for reducing inflammation and swelling. Excellent for herpes, ulcers, soreness and burns. Quince face packs are excellent for open pores: the fruit is cut into thin slices, put into a glass jar with 50 per cent alcohol and kept covered in a dark place for a week. Cotton wool soaked in the decanted liquid is applied to the face and left on for 15 minutes, then the pack is removed and the face washed with warm water.

Other Uses: The firm, aromatic, pectin-rich quince pulp is used to make jams, marmalades and jellies.

Lemon Grass

Gramineae

Cymbopogon nardus (L.) Rendle

Description: A fragrant tropical grass 120−150 cm high, forming massive tufts. Reproduced by root division, as it rarely forms seeds.

Origin and Distribution: Native to tropical Asia where it has long been grown around houses as a simple means of perfuming the air. Several varieties are cultivated in plantations in Indonesia and Sri Lanka.

Harvesting and Preparation: The leaves are mown, usually 10 months after planting, then at approximately four-monthly intervals, depending on the weather. Each mowing yields about 12−14 tons of grass per hectare, so three times that amount can be harvested in a year. Under primitive cultivation conditions, without fertilizing the soil, the plantation must be transferred to another plot every four to five years.

Constituents: All species of the *Cymbopogon* genus (altogether about 30) secrete a volatile oil from the leaf blades, sheaths and husks. *Cymbopogon nardus* and *Cymbopogon winterianus,* known only as cultivated varieties, contain 0.5 to 1 per cent citronella oil *(Oleum citronellae).* The volatile oil consists of 25−50 per cent citronellal, 25−40 per cent geraniol, and citral. *Cymbopogon martini* is the source of the so-called palmarose oil and *Cymbopogon flexuosus* produces the so-called lemon grass oil, or citronella.

Cosmetic Uses: All the above-mentioned oils are important raw materials in the perfume industry, being essential ingredients in most of the well-known perfumes and cosmetics. These volatile oils are relatively rare and are therefore expensive.

Other Uses: The name 'lemon grass' refers to all citronella species; in Malaysia and India they are used as a seasoning in spice mixtures to make them smell of lemon. They are used for flavouring soups, sauces, fish dishes and for the preparation of tea.

Globe Artichoke

Compositae

Cynara scolimus L.

Description: A robust perennial plant forming massive underground roots and reaching an average height of 1.5 m. Leaves are pinnately divided, greyish on the reverse. The branched stems bear large decorative, violet-blue thistle-like flowers in terminal heads, in July and August.

Distribution: Probably native to northern Africa, and brought to Europe by Arabs, to France and Spain. Now cultivated throughout Europe.

Constituents: Globe artichokes, like cardoons (*Cynara cardunculus* L.) to which they are related, contain the pleasantly bitter cynarine, a derivative of caffeic acid. It is reliable gall-bladder drug, and is often successful in treating colic. It also has a diuretic effect. It is also used for jaundice and other liver disorders.

Cosmetic Uses: As with carrots, tomatoes and other vegetables, the vitamins and trace elements (minerals, organic acids, pigments, etc.) in artichokes make them a useful addition to skin cleansers, tonics and lotions, regenerative creams and face packs.

Other Uses: Globe artichokes are popular as a vegetable, especially in France and other Mediterranean countries. The edible parts of the flowerheads, which are eaten at the bud stage, are the pulpy base of each scale and the heart at the base of the flower. They were eaten in ancient Greek and Roman times, when they were served as a delicacy at noblemen's feasts.

94

Carrot
Umbelliferae

Daucus carota L.

Description: The cultivated carrot is a biennial plant with a thick, pulpy, usually orange taproot and petiolate, segmented leaves. In the second year an erect stem, branched in its upper part, appears and terminates with an umbel of yellow-white flowers flowering from May till August. The fruit is a spiny achene. The wild carrot, from which the cultivated variety derives, is a common European weed.

Origin, Cultivation and Harvesting: Native to Europe, and cultivated since pre-Roman times. There are many varieties, short- and long-rooted, available in white, yellow, orange, violet, and red. The part used is the taproot, harvested in the first year.

Constituents: The carrot is an important raw material cosmetically, as it contains large quantities of provitamin A, carotenes, other carotenoids, vitamin B_1 and B_2, vitamin C, a small amount of volatile oil, saccharides and pectins. Both medicinally and cosmetically, the anti-inflammatory effects of these substances, combined with the effects of vitamin A and β-carotene in improving the protective and healing ability of the skin against infection, injury and inflammation are of great value.

Cosmetic Uses: The cosmetic industry manufactures stabilized carrot extract which is added to products such as skin creams, face lotions, packs and protective suntan creams. Preparations containing carrot extract improve the physiological function of the skin, restore its elasticity and help keep it soft and smooth. The simple home-made face pack can be made from fresh grated carrot. After washing the face thoroughly, apply to the skin and leave on for 20 minutes. Remove with warm water and apply a rich or half-dry cream. Preparations for children and infants often contain carrot extract. The volatile oil from carrot achenes is used in perfume industry.

Other Uses: The carrot is of course a popular root vegetable, but it is also an effective remedy for diarrhoea and digestive disorders. Its carotene content enables the body to make vitamin A, important for good vision.

Borneo Camphor

Dipterocarpaceae

Dryobalanops aromatica Gaertn. fil.

Description: A tall tree with leathery leaves on long petioles, usually with stipules. The fragrant flowers are arranged in elongated clusters. The fruit is a nut covered with a leathery rind, and has elongated points on the calyx which aid the dissemination of the seeds by air.

Origin and Distribution: Native to Malaysia where it is cultivated for its volatile oil containing camphor. According to place of origin this is known as Sumatra or Borneo camphor; in Malaysian it is called 'kajoe kapur'.

Processing and Preparation: As with the genuine camphor tree, the volatile oil is obtained from the cut wood of older trees and distilled with steam.

Constituents: The composition of camphor oil from *Dryobalanops* is very similar to that obtained from the camphor tree. It contains 35 per cent terpenes (pinen, camphene, dipentene), 10 per cent alcohols (borneol, terpineol), 20 per cent sesquiterpenes, and various resins.

Cosmetic Uses: Used in the same way as genuine camphor, in toothpastes, mouthwashes, lotions, aftershaves, massage creams, shampoos and bath additives. As camphor oil from *Dryobalanops aromatica* is rare and not often available on the world market, its use as an aromatic in cosmetics is limited. The trade is in the hands of Chinese dealers and it is processed mainly locally and exported in the form of local special products.

Other Uses: In Malaysia, Borneo and Sumatra camphor is used for embalming and ritual purposes, and is highly valued. Not all the wood is processed for camphor; being of high quality, coarse-grained and easy to work, it is used for building houses, bridges and ships.

98

Field Horsetail

Equisetaceae

Equisetum arvense L.

Description: A perennial plant with a string-like, jointed rootstock growing deep in the ground. From it rise shoots of two very different kinds. In spring, fertile shooots about 15 cm high appear; these are unbranched, beige to red-brown, terminating with a cylindrical, cone-like spike within which spores are formed. These shoots grow in March and April. After releasing the spores the spring shoots die and are replaced by sterile, green summer shoots about 20 cm high, with whorls of thin, rough, grooved branches.

Distribution: Common in most of the temperate zone in the northern hemisphere, and also found in northern and southern Africa and the Canary Islands. Likes moist clay and sandy soil. Can be a troublesome weed.

Harvesting and Preparation: Sterile shoots are gathered from June to September and dried in an airy place. When dried artificially the temperature must not exceed 40° C.

Constituents: Sterile green shoots contain 6−8 per cent partially soluble silicic acid, 5 per cent saponin equisetine, flavone, glycosides with the aglycones quercetine, luteolin, campherol, traces of volatile oil and alkaloids.

Cosmetic Uses: A lukewarm infusion (20 g of the dried herb to 100 ml of boiling water and extracted for 20 minutes) may be used for washing tired, ageing and problem skins. Horsetail baths should be taken every night before going to bed, for at least a week at a time. After the bath a nutritious cream should be applied. A horsetail bath can also be taken in the morning. This will close the pores and tighten the skin. To make a skin lotion from horsetail, mix 6 parts of horsetail infusion with 3.5 parts diluted alcohol or cologne and 5 parts of 8 per cent vinegar or boric acid diluted with water. Horsetail extract is contained in cleansing preparations for greasy skin with impurities such as pimples, acne, and boils. Decoctions are also used in hair rinses and tonic foam baths.

Other Uses: Horsetail is used medicinally as a diuretic and to stabilize scar tissue in mild cases of tuberculosis.

Blue Gum

Myrtaceae

Eucalyptus globulus Labill.

Description: Like numerous other species of this genus, *Eucalyptus globulus* is a robust, evergreen tree about 70 m high. The young leaves are opposite, sessile, cordiform-ovoid, and hoary blue in colour, while older leaves are alternate, 15−25 cm long, narrow and curved like a sickle. Large solitary white flowers appear in the leaf axils. They have a woody calyx, which forms a peripheral circular collar, and a corolla forming a thick, dish-like conical cap which falls off after the stamens unfold. All parts of the tree are abundantly permeated with cells bearing the pungent volatile oil.

Origin and Distribution: All eucalyptus species are native to Australia, although in the Tertiary Period they also grew in Europe. They are also commonly grown in Africa, the Middle East, North and South America, and Asia. They can survive an annual rainfall of less than 500 mm, but require moist soil.

Constituents: The leaves are the main source of the volatile oil (2−3 per cent), obtained by distillation with steam. Its main component is cineol, also called eucalyptol (70−85 per cent), which is frozen out of the volatile oil. Sometimes the volatile oil contains piperiton or phellandrene instead of or besides cineol. Apart from volatile oil, the leaves contain a considerable amount of tannin.

Cosmetic Uses: Pure cineol is an ingredient of massage creams used to improve blood circulation, and of aftershaves and other cosmetics for men. It is an important ingredient of toothpastes and mouthwashes, bath additives and deodorant sprays. To a lesser extent it is used in soaps, skin creams and shampoos. Some eucalyptus oils, especially those from *Eucalyptus macarthuri* and *Eucalyptus citriodora* contain large amounts of fragrant substances such as citral, citronellal and geraniol acetate, which are used in the perfume industry.

Other Uses: In medicine eucalyptus oil is used for its antiseptic and expectorant properties, mainly in vapour baths for asthma and inflammations of the upper respiratory tract, in pastilles for colds and sore throats, and in anti-rheumatic ointments. The wood is also of great value. Gum-trees grow quickly and dry out swampy soils, and they are planted in warm swampy regions as a part of malaria control.

Meadow Eyebright

Scrophulariaceae

Euphrasia rostkoviana Hayne

Description: An annual plant with a branched root, whose secondary rootlets feed on the roots of other plants. The plant is a semiparasite. The leafy stem is erect, branched all the way up, about 20−30 cm high, and covered with soft hairs. The leaves are opposite, without petioles, and deeply cut. The two-lipped flowers are usually white flecked with yellow on the lower lip, sometimes light violet, about 1 cm long, arranged in spikes.

Distribution: Grows throughout Europe, in damp meadows, pastures and other grassy areas in lowlands and mountains.

Harvesting and Preparation: The whole flowering herb is gathered, tied in bunches and dried in the shade, at temperatures up to 40° C. There are many other species of eyebright, and their differentiation is difficult, e. g. *Euphrasia stricta* is gathered and used in the same way as the meadow eyebright.

Constituents: Not all the plant's active substances are known and so many of its effects are uncertain. It is, however, effective against inflammations, as a disinfectant, and for contracting the pores of the skin. Substances isolated so far are aucubin (a glycoside), specific tannins, resins with an antibacterial effect, traces of a volatile oil of unknown composition and provitamin A.

Cosmetic Uses: A meadow eyebright infusion (20 g of the herb to 100 cc hot water, extracted until cool) mixed with the same amount of diluted boric acid can be used on cotton-wool for wiping the eyes in cases of inflammation and eye-strain, and to remove eye make-up. Meadow eyebright extract is also added to some skin astringents used for healing skin blemishes.

Other Uses: Although in folk medicine, meadow eyebright is used as an eye-wash for eye infections, in orthodox medicine it is not used, as its composition is still insufficiently known. Nevertheless, it may be widely used for these purposes in the future.

Fennel

Umbelliferae

Foeniculum vulgare Mill.

Description: A biennial plant, sometimes living three to four years under favourable conditions. Stem up to 1.5−2 m high. Leaves are finely divided into many threadlike segments, on long, membranous sheaths. Large, flat, compound umbels of yellow flowers appear from July to October. Fruit is an oblong, 5-ribbed diachene, about 8 mm long and 3 mm wide, green, greenish-yellow or brownish. They have a strong scent and a pleasant, spicy, somewhat sweetish taste.

Distribution: The plant grows wild in southern Europe, and is extensively cultivated in Europe, the USA, India and Japan. It prefers warmer regions with a long, dry and warm summer, but is quite hardy.

Cultivation: Fennel has long been cultivated for its seeds and leaves. Several varieties are known, including *F. dulce* or Florence fennel, which yields, besides the achenes, a swollen leaf base which is a delicate vegetable.

Constituents: The active substance in the achenes is the volatile oil (2.5−6 per cent), containing anethole, fenchene and other accompanying substances. The bitter fenchene is not present in the volatile oil of Florence fennel. The achenes also contain fats (12−18 per cent parsley oil compounds) and proteins (14−22 per cent).

Cosmetic Uses: A fennel infusion (10 g to 100 cc boiling water, extracted for 20 minutes) makes a good face lotion for greasy skin. (Sensitive skin, however, does not tolerate fennel infusion and may develop allergies.) Fennel infusion is also recommended for washing greasy hair (increasing hair gloss and giving the hair a pleasant smell) and as an ingredient of tonic baths. Fennel oil or anethole alone is used in aromatic mixtures for toothpastes, mouthwashes, soaps and aftershaves.

Other Uses: Fennel oil is used medicinally for inflammations of the upper respiratory tract; an infusion taken internally allays gastro-intestinal disorders such as colic, cramps and flatulence. In cooking, fennel seeds and leaves are good in all kinds of fish dishes.

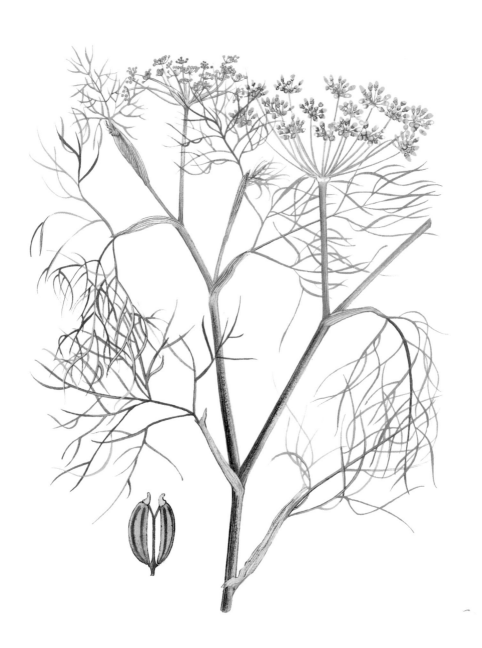

Wild Strawberry

Rosaceae

Fragaria vesca L.

Description: A perennial plant with a branching rootstock; from it rises a basal rosette of ternate leaves on long petioles, and fruiting stalks growing only slightly above the leaves. Stems are poorly branched, bearing several white flowers which appear successively from April till August. Numerous tiny ovaries ripening into strawberries (which are false fruits; actually enlarged pulpy receptacles holding numerous seed-like achenes). Ripe strawberries are pleasantly sweet and juicy with a delicious scent.

Origin and Distribution: Native to Europe and temperate regions of Asia, growing in clearings, deciduous woodland, on stony hillsides, in ditches and meadows. Found in lowlands as well as in mountains.

Preparation: Strawberry leaves, especially the young ones, are gathered during the flowering period and dried in shade.

Constituents: Tannins (7−10 per cent), volatile citral smelling of lemons, flavone compounds, organic acids, vitamin C and phytoncides.

Cosmetic Uses: An infusion (50 g of leaves to 200 ml of boiling water, extracted for about 30 minutes) cleanses the skin and contracts the pores. The juice from the fruit is recommended as an ingredient of face creams for its regenerating and tonic effects, and strawberry pulp may be used as a face pack, but for these purposes the cultivated strawberry varieties are usually used.

Other Uses: Because of its tannin content, strawberry-leaf tea is drunk as an intestinal tonic and a mild diuretic. Strawberry leaves form part of the German 'medicinal' herb tea *'Species germanicae'*. Fermented leaves are recommended as a palatable substitute for genuine tea when the latter is forbidden because of its caffeine content. Wild strawberries are palatable and aromatic, both fresh and preserved.

Common Fumitory

Papaveraceae

Fumaria officinalis L.

Description: An annual plant 10−30 cm high with a hollow, angular, richly foliate stem. Leaves are light green, petiolate, fine, composed of oblong linear leaflets. Flowers are tubular, with a long spur, arranged in sparse racemes, pale to purple-red, appearing from May till July.

Distribution: A common weed native from lowland to mountain regions in Europe, western Asia and northern Africa, and introduced with grain to all continents. Grows in fields and gardens, along waysides and on waste ground.

Harvesting and Preparation: The flowering herb is gathered in May − July, and dried as quickly as possible, in shade.

Constituents: The herb contains the alkaloids corydaline, protopine, bulbocapinine and dicentrine, bitter substances, organic acids and mineral substances.

Cosmetic Uses: An infusion (20 g of herb to 200 ml of hot water extracted for 20 minutes) may be drunk for skin problems such as those associated with impurities, and also used for washing. A mixture of fresh fumitory and yarrow juices, mixed with wheat flour to make a paste, may be used as a face pack for greasy skin with acne and clogged pores. The juice is prepared by grinding the two fresh herbs in a pestle and mortar, adding a little water and pressing through a cloth. Flour is added to form a fairly stiff paste, applied to the face and allowed to dry. Then it is washed off with lukewarm water. The procedure should be repeated every other day until the skin is clear.

Other Uses: In medicine fumitory is used to a limited extent in the treatment of digestive and gall-bladder disorders. In folk medicine it is used for liver diseases, gastric ulcers, constipation, and inflammations of the urinary tract.

Woodruff

Rubiaceae

Galium odoratum (L.) Scop.
syn. *Asperula odorata* L.

Description: A perennial plant with a thin, cylindrical, trailing rootstock and a quadrangular, glabrous stem 10−30 cm high. Bright green, elongated, rough-edged, tapering leaves are arranged in whorls. Fragrant tiny white flowers arranged in cymose panicles appear in May and June. Fruit is a globose, bristly diachene.

Distribution: Occurs throughout the whole of northern and central Europe, Siberia and northern Africa. Grows in shady forests, particularly beech forests, but also in coniferous forests, usually abundantly. Found in lowlands and mountainous regions.

Harvesting and Preparation: The herb is gathered shortly before it flowers. It must be dried as quickly as possible, in shade, because it browns easily.

Constituents: The main active substance of the herb is coumarine which gives it its characteristic smell. It is a glycosidically bound compound, quite common in the vegetable kingdom. Woodruff contains a relatively high quantity (0.9 per cent) of coumarine which is formed during drying, being absent in the fresh plant. Its pharmacological effect consists in reducing the clotting capacity of the blood. Coumarine, together with the tannins in the plant, also affects skin pigmentation; both these properties can be used in cosmetics.

Cosmetic Uses: Woodruff infusion (10 g to 100 cc boiling water, extracted for 10 minutes) drunk as a tea can be used for improving blood circulation and to darken plain, pale skin slightly. A woodruff bath must not be combined with sunbathing. The skin must not be exposed to sun for at least an hour after washing. If no allergic symptoms (swellings or a rash) appear, woodruff may be taken for about two months, alternating a week's applications with a week's intermission. As a natural fragrance coumarine is used in the perfume industry.

Other Uses: In some regions, especially those where wine is grown, a so-called May potion is prepared, even today. The fresh herb is gathered before flowering and eluted in slightly sweetened wine. This same May potion was mentioned by the Benedictine Wandalbertus in AD 854.

Witch Hazel

Hamamelis virginiana L.

Hamamelidaceae

Description: A deciduous shrub or small tree with scaly bark, approximately 5 m high. Leaves are similar to hazel leaves, coarsely toothed with 5 – 7 pairs of veins, finely hairy on the reverse. Bright yellow flowers have narrow, band-like petals and grow in clusters in the leaf axils. Buds are spirally coiled like a watch spring. Flowers in autumn and winter, sometimes as late as February. Flowering lasts until all the leaves have fallen. Fruit is an ovoid capsule bearing two black seeds.

Origin and Distribution: Native to the eastern part of North America, from Nova Scotia to Florida and Texas. Related species used in the same way are grown in Asia: *Hamamelis mollis* in central China and *Hamamelis japonica* in Japan.

Preparation: Mainly the dried leaves, and to a lesser extent the bark and young shoots of the shrubs, are used.

Constituents: The leaves contain about 8 per cent tannins (mainly β-hamamelitannin), flavone glycosides and saponins. These substances have an astringent effect on the skin.

Cosmetic Uses: Stabilized extracts of witch hazel are prepared mainly for their astringent effect and are added to the many cosmetic products. Besides contracting the skin, witch hazel has a favourable effect on blemished, impure skin with very dilated pores and inhibits excessive sebum secretion. Extracts of the herb are therefore added to day and night creams, anti-perspirants, face powders, bath additives and face packs. Medicated water obtained by the distillation of fresh leaves, bark and young shoots with steam is recommended for washing.

Other Uses: Therapeutically important because of its high tannin content. Extracts are added to ointments for frostbite, haemorrhoids, varicose ulcers, insect bites and stings, minor burns and bruises. Numerous *Hamamelis* species are grown as ornamental shrubs and trees.

Ivy

Araliaceae

Hedera helix L.

Description: An evergreen climber clinging to surfaces by means of adventitious roots. The woody stem is much branched, the leaves conspicuously dimorphous: on the sterile, trailing stems the leaves are alternate, palmately lobed, leathery and glossy with marked light venation; the fertile, erect stems bear narrow, ovoid leaves growing in a spiral around the axis; the venation is inconspicuous. On the fertile branches no adventitious roots occur. Flowers are yellowish green, in umbels, appearing from August to October. The fruit is a black berry which ripens in winter.

Origin and Distribution: Indigenous to Europe but also common in Asia, and introduced to North America. Abundant in shady woods where it climbs up tree trunks.

Constituents: For cosmetic and medicinal purposes older, palmately lobed leaves are used. They contain 4 per cent saponins, which unblock respiratory tracts in cases of catarrh and colds; they also have an antispasmodic effect. The dosage must be determined by a doctor, as high doses of the drug are toxic, especially the berries.

Cosmetic Uses: May be used as a wash for swellings, sores, dandruff and other skin problems. Stabilized ivy extract is applied in the forms of creams and lotions. Very effective are ivy face packs prepared from washed, ground ivy leaves and applied for a maximum of 15 minutes on the affected area. After the application the skin should be lightly and briefly wiped with a damp cloth soaked in ethanol. NB The leaves may cause dermatitis in sensitive people.

Other Uses: Cuttings from young plants are used to obtain trailing or climbing plants; cuttings from older, fertile plants produce erect plants. Various leaf forms of ivy, including those with mottled leaves, are grown as ornamentals. Ivy is very effective as ground cover in gardens and for covering large vertical areas with a green screen. The wood is used in woodcarving in the same way as box wood *(Buxus)*.

Rose-mallow

Malvaceae

Hibiscus abelmoschus L.

Description: An annual plant up to 2 m high, with alternate, petiolate, sharply lobed, toothed leaves. Flowers have five yellow petals and reddish-purple centres. Ovary ripens into a hairy pyramidal capsule with greyish-yellow, kidney-shaped seeds the size of peas.

Origin and Distribution: Native to eastern India and cultivated elsewhere, mostly in southern Asia and South America.

Harvesting and Preparation: Grown for its musky seeds, called ambrette, or musk-seeds *(Grana moschata).* Dry seeds are gathered and pulverized.

Constituents: Ground seeds yield 0.2−0.6 per cent volatile oil obtained by distillation with steam. The volatile oil is light yellow, dense, with a musky smell; consists of farnesol, ambrettolid, esters of acetic, ambrettolic and (unless of liquid consistency) palmitine acids.

Cosmetic Uses: Used in fragrances made for perfuming face creams, gels, lipsticks, grease-paints, face lotions, aftershaves, powders, etc. Also used in perfumes for men and oriental perfumes.

Other Uses: The immature fruit of rose-mallow is a palatable vegetable, as is the fruit of the related species *Hibiscus esculentus* (okra). The plant fibres can be spun as hemp, as can those of the closely related species *Hibiscus cannabinus.* The red-flowered *Hibiscus sabdariffa,* native to the Sudan and cultivated in the tropics, contains the so-called hibiscus flowers, numerous organic acids, including hibiscus acid (hydrooxycitric-lactone). In the Orient the flowers are used for the preparation of an excellent refreshing drink (karkade). Because of its moderately laxative effects it is suitable for taking as part of slimming diets.

Hop

Cannabinaceae

Humulus lupulus L.

Description: A vigorous perennial climber with a prostrate, branching root-stock and numerous roots. Stems are up to 6 m long, twining, square and tough, covered with rough, spiky hairs. The rough leaves on long petioles are variable in shape, from cordate to three-lobed, coarsely serrate. The hop has separate male and female plants, flowering from May till July. The yellow male flowers are arranged in axillary or apical clusters. The female flowers are pendulous, scaly, cone-like, light green during flowering time, pale yellow when mature, bearing golden-yellow glands filled with lupulin. In hop gardens only the female plants are cultivated, as only the fruits, or hops, are used.

Distribution: The wild hop grows throughout the temperate zone of the northern hemisphere, usually in moist places such as thickets along brooks and rivers.

Harvesting and Preparation: Only the female fruits, or hops, are gathered; sterile fruits from cultivated hops are more valuable than wild ones. They are picked at the end of August and carefully dried at 40−50° C.

Constituents: Up to 1 per cent volatile oil, consisting mainly of myrcene (30−50 per cent), β-caryophyllene (20−40 per cent), dipentene, humulene, linalool and geraniol. Also important components of the volatile oil are resins, with the specific bitter substances humulone, cohumulone, lupulone, colupulone and xanthohumulone.

Cosmetic Uses: The oestrogens contained in hops are used cosmetically for slowing down and delaying the skin ageing process. The discovery of this property is by no means a new one; brewery sludge was used in the Middle Ages for rejuvenating baths (the so-called 'fountains of youth'). Hop extracts are used in creams, face lotions and milks for sensitive skin, and for sagging and impure skin, as an ingredient in soothing and regenerative baths. Also, most importantly, hops are used in special 'beer shampoos' intended to prevent brittleness and make the hair glossy. Beer as such can be successfully used as a hair rinse.

Other Uses: Hops are important mainly for the production of beer, a popular beverage throughout the world. Hops are used medicinally in sedatives and mild hypnotics and regulators of the digestive processes.

Perforate St John's Wort

Hypericaceae

Hypericum perforatum L.

Description: A perennial plant with a profusely branched rootstock and an erect stem up to 60 cm high, branching at the top. Leaves are opposite, oblong to linear with transparent spots which are glands bearing volatile oil. Flowers 20−25 mm across appear from May till September, arranged in rich panicles. The golden-yellow five-petalled flowers are dotted with black glands at the edges, and when broken these glands exude a dark red oil. The fruit is a capsule.

Distribution: Grows in Europe, eastern North America, Asia and northern Africa. Abundant on sunny slopes, dry meadows, pastures, in thickets, but also found in peat-bogs and waste ground, from lowlands to mountains.

Harvesting and Preparation: The tops of flowering plants, about 20−30 cm long, are cut, bound into bundles and hung up to dry quickly.

Constituents: The herb contains catechin tannins, flavone glycosides (hyperoside, rutin, quercitrine, red pigments hypericine, pseudohypericine) and 0.1 per cent volatile oil.

Cosmetic Uses: With the reddish oil extracted from this plant cosmetics with healing and regenerative effects are manufactured. The oil extract mixed with avocado oil, wheat-germ and carrot oil is highly recommended as regenerative skin oil, and it is also suitable for creams and emulsions. The home-made oil (fresh flowers are poured over with vegetable oil and extracted with an occasional shaking for about 10 days) is recommended for the treatment of dry, cracked skin, and for refining of the skin and soothing inflammation.

Other Uses: Therapeutically it is considered a sedative (especially for the gastro-intestinal and urinary tracts) as well as a drug with healing effects. Folk medicine ascribed to it miraculous effects, connected with the superstition about 'St John's blood' which was thought to be exuded by the plant.

Florentine Iris

Iridaceae

Iris florentina L.

Description: A perennial plant with a branched, tuberous, trailing rhizome and grey-green, sword-like leaves. Stem is up to 100 cm long, branched at the top, terminating in a tubular flower with three outer petals bent backwards and three inner ones bent upwards towards one another. Flowers are white or blue, the outer petals with yellow hairs, and appear in May and June. The fruit is a large capsule with numerous seeds.

Distribution: Known as a cultivated plant for over 2,000 years, and now cultivated mainly in France and Italy. Of the numerous species of iris the following are important for perfumery: *Iris florentina, Iris germanica* and *Iris pallida*. All three differ in flower colour, and are native to southern Europe.

Harvesting and Preparation: In the third or fourth year after planting the rhizomes (called orris root) of cultivated plants are gathered. They are dug up in August, quickly washed and peeled. It is best to dry them artificially, at temperatures of up to 40° C. The violet scent develops during drying.

Constituents: Peeled dried rhizomes contain mostly starch and mucilages, as well as 0.1−0.2 per cent volatile oil containing the violet-scented irone (10 per cent). The fragrance appears only during the drying process and is not present in fresh rhizomes.

Cosmetic Uses: Three types of substances have a characteristic violet scent: the volatile oil from violet flowers, irones from iris rhizomes and synthetic ionones. Violet perfumes are very popular and iris oil is therefore very important in the perfume and cosmetic industries. It is used for perfuming face creams, lotions, milks, lipsticks, grease-paints, soaps, oils, brilliantines, powders and shampoos. Pure irone and synthetic ionones are used in the same way.

Other Uses: May be added to teas for bronchitis, coughs and sore throats.

Jasmine

Oleaceae

Jasminum grandiflorum L.

Description: A vine-like deciduous shrub with long, smooth, slender, twining branches. The leaves are opposite, composed of 5−7 elliptical or oval-pointed leaflets, 15−40 mm long. The sweet-smelling white flowers about 35 mm across grow on thin pedicels, and are arranged in sparse racemes.

Origin and Distribution: Native to Asia, from Iran to China. Its fragrant flowers make it popular in gardens in mild districts and in greenhouses in cooler districts.

Harvesting: Only the flowers are gathered; they are not dried but processed while still fresh. Flowers of other jasmine species are also gathered: the white-flowered *Jasminum auriculatum* from Sri Lanka, *Jasminum gracile* from Australia, *Jasminum gracillium* from Borneo and *Jasminum dichotonum* from western Africa (flowers of the latter species open only at night). The flowers of some other species have pink or yellow flowers.

Constituents: The flowers contain volatile oil, the main components of which are benzyl acetate, benzyl alcohol, iasmone, eugenol and farnesol. The amount of the individual components varies according to place of origin. Approximately 4,000 kg of volatile oil from different species are produced annually.

Cosmetic Uses: Jasmine oil is very important in the perfume industry, for the preparation of jasmine perfume itself and for perfuming many cosmetic preparations. Jasmine perfume is a complex mixture of 6 basic, 21 nuancing, 18 active and 8 fixing substances. It forms part of Chanel No. 5. Jasmine perfume is used in many skin creams, gels, lotions, lipsticks, soaps, brilliantines and powders.

Other Uses: Often grown as an ornamental shrub.

Walnut

Juglans regia L.

Juglandaceae

Description: A large, wide-branched tree up to 45 m high, with brownish-grey cracked bark. The leaves are deciduous, unpaired pinnate, releasing a pleasant smell when rubbed between the fingers. Male and female flowers appear on the same tree, the male flowers in dense, pendulous catkins, formed at the ends of the previous year's branches, the female flowers in sparse terminal spikes. The fruits are plum-shaped and yellowish-green on the surface, containing a 'nut' with a thick, rugged 'shell' protecting the edible seed.

Origin and Distribution: Indigenous to mountain forests from the Balkans to eastern Asia, but widely cultivated throughout the temperate zone.

Constituents: Two parts of the walnut tree yield useful substances, the leathery leaves which are gathered in summer, and the dried green shell of immature fruits. The leaves contain approximately 13 per cent tannins, a small amount of volatile oil, and glycide, converted after leaf-tissue damage into a brown staining substance called juglone. The dried fruit shell contains, besides oils and tannins, a relatively large amount of vitamin C.

Cosmetic Uses: The colouring properties of juglone are of cosmetic use, both in suntan oils and creams and in shampoos and hair tints to achieve beautiful brown tinges. Hair can be tinted at home with the fresh juice from the green shells surrounding the nuts. Mix about 20 g of ground green walnut husks with 50 cc water, 25 g alum and 75 g salad oil. Warm the mixture gently until it has the required tinge, and apply to the hair. The juice must be fresh, as it loses its tinting properties very quickly. It can also be used mixed with ethyl alcohol (10 g ground green husks in 100 cc 60 per cent ethanol).

Other Uses: In medicine the tannin content of walnut is utilized, internally in chronic enteritis and externally in baths for itching eczemas and frostbite. Walnut trees are of course grown mainly for their palatable oily seeds and for their hard, heavy and very durable wood which is used in shipbuilding and the manufacture of furniture.

Sweet Bay, Bay Laurel

Lauraceae

Laurus nobilis L.

Description: An evergreen tree or shrub 2−5 m high. Leaves are leathery, oblong-lanceolate, with wavy edges, dark green, glossy above, reverse lighter, with prominent venation. Usually 6−7 cm long, 2−3 cm wide, having a pleasant smell and bitter taste. Flowers are small, whitish or yellowish. Fruit is a red-blue berry containing a single oily seed.

Distribution: Found wild in Asia Minor and the Mediterranean region, and cultivated elsewhere. (The ceremonial laurel of ancient times being the symbol of power and glory.)

Harvesting and Preparation: Leaves and berries are used for their aromatic properties. Ripe berries are picked and expressed for their oil, coloured green by the presence of chlorophyll. Leaves at least 2 years old are gathered by hand in autumn and slowly dried in shade, in thin layers.

Constituents: The leaves contain up to 3 per cent volatile oil composed of cineole, eugenol, pinene, linalool and geraniol, as well as tannins, bitter substances and other oils. The fruit contains up to 10 per cent volatile oil containing cineole but no eugenol.

Cosmetic Uses: Bay may be used externally to disinfect and improve blood circulation to the skin. These and its pleasant smelling aromatic properties make it useful as a bath additive. About a handful of leaves wrapped in a cloth is put into a hot bath and left to extract until the bath cools down. After the bath the skin turns rosy, brightens up and the pores contract quickly. For the treatment of itching rashes or fungal diseases of the feet a decoction of bay leaves or berries (50 g boiled in a litre of water for about 10 minutes) may be added to the bath. It is advisable to take the bath daily for about 15 minutes until relief is felt, and then once every three days for about two weeks.

Other Uses: Bay leaves are one of the oldest and most popular culinary herbs. It is often grown simply for decoration.

Lavender

Labiatae

Lavandula officinalis Chaix.

Description: A pleasantly aromatic, profusely branched subshrub, about 60 cm high, woody at the base. Leaves are sessile, linear, the young ones grey and downy, older ones greenish. Violet-blue tubular flowers are arranged in successive whorls at the top of the stem, appearing from June till August.

Origin, Distribution and Cultivation: Native to southern Europe where it still grows wild. Also grown as cultivated plant everywhere along the Mediterranean and elsewhere in Europe, also in Asia and the USA. Lavender requires light chalky soil and is cultivated from seed or by root division or cuttings. Lives for about six to seven years.

Harvesting and Preparation: Either just the flowers or the whole flowering plants are gathered at the beginning of the flowering period, in dry weather when the plants contain the maximum amounts of aromatic substances. Lavender is still often cut by hand, but in some countries the harvesting is mechanized. In France the herb is cut and distilled immediately in the field in mobile distillation columns, to avoid loss of the fragrant volatile oil during drying. Flowers and the whole herb must be dried in shade.

Constituents: Lavender oil consists of 50 per cent linalool compounds, mainly of linalool acetate. It also contains cineole and geraniol in significant amounts.

Cosmetic Uses: Lavender has long been cultivated for its perfume. Its Latin name is derived from *lavare,* meaning to wash. It was used in ancient Rome as a fragrant, refreshing bath additive and is still used for this purpose. The volatile oil is used in soaps, face lotions and creams, bath additives and spray deodorants. In perfumery it is the basic substance used to make Fougère and many other perfumes, and a nuancer for cologne, chypre and Russia leather. England became especially renowned for the manufacture of lavender water and perfume, as lavender was the most popular scent, particularly in Victorian times.

Lavender should not be used in face packs, as it irritates the skin. The species *Lavandula latifolia* yields a volatile oil called spike oil, resembling that obtained from *L. officinalis,* but with a more herbal character. Another related volatile oil, the so-called lavandin oil, is obtained from a hybrid called lavandin, which is extensively grown in Spain and France.

Henna

Lythraceae

Lawsonia inermis L.

Description: An evergreen, low to medium-high shrub (3−6 m), with small, narrow, elliptical leaves. The flowers are whitish, pink to brick-red and grow in large terminal panicles diffusing a pleasant, intense smell. The fruit is a small capsule.

Distribution: Frequently cultivated, this is a common species in arid regions of northern and eastern tropical Africa, Madagascar, tropical Asia, Sri Lanka, Australia and tropical America. Particularly important in Muslim culture. Often planted in hedges, for its showy appearance and fragrant flowers.

Harvesting and Preparation: Cultivated from seed. Harvesting can begin when the plants are about three years old: young shoots are cut in lengths of 20−25 cm, dried and ground. From 1 hectare 1.5 to 2 tons of the plant can be harvested annually.

Constituents: Besides a considerable quantity of tannins, the leaves contain a substance called lawson, chemically 2-hydroxy-1-4-naphtoquinone. This gives henna its dyeing properties (in the Orient it is also called *hennah, henne* or *hinne*). The red-yellow to yellow-brown dye is obtained by adding basic lime milk to the leaves.

Cosmetic Uses: Henna is a very old oriental dye, used for tinting the hair, beard, eyelashes, skin and nails. It is the oldest decorative cosmetic of the Old World, and is still used in cosmetics today. Powdered henna is mixed with water to make a paste which is applied to the hair. Henna alone tints the hair red to auburn. Mixed with indigo − which is a deep blue dyestuff obtained from the plant *Indigofera tinctoria* − it colours the hair various shades of brown to black. For tinting the hair black, henna is mixed with indigo in the ratio of 1:3. From *Lawsonia* flowers fragrant volatile oil is distilled and used in oriental perfumes.

Other Uses: Because of its tannin content henna was once widely used for dyeing leather and fabrics. Ancient Egyptian mummies were often wrapped in cloths dyed with henna. The Arabs often use henna for colouring horses' hoofs, tails and manes.

Lovage

Umbelliferae

Levisticum officinale L.

Description: A perennial plant with a thick, short, pulpy rootstock and long, branched, yellow-brown roots which are white inside and very aromatic. From the rootstock rise glossy, dark green basal leaves on long petioles, deeply divided into several leaflets. Stem is 1−2 m high, foliate; upper leaves grow on short petioles. The large, dense umbels of yellow flowers grow in the leaf axils and appear in July and August.

Origin and Distribution: Comes from western Asia, but also grows wild in Europe. Cultivated in many European countries at all altitudes, in gardens from which it spread to meadows and fields.

Harvesting and Preparation: The rhizomes and roots of two- to three-year-old plants are gathered in September and October. The overground parts are removed and the remainder cleaned and dried at temperatures not exceeding 40° C. For home use the leaves are also gathered at flowering time and dried in shade.

Constituents: The rootstock contains volatile oil (0.5−1 per cent), composed of 70 per cent butylphthalides and their derivates, α-terpineol, carvacrol, coumarin and traces of butyric acid. It also contains bitter substances, organic acids and sugars.

Cosmetic Uses: The pungent smell of lovage oil cannot be considered a pleasant perfume by itself, but the oil has been used in some modern perfume compositions. Lovage root is of use as a bath additive for its beneficial effect on blood circulation, for its moderately stimulant properties and in foot-baths for fungal diseases.

Other Uses: In medicine the underground parts of the plant are valued for their diuretic properties. The drug is administered internally, in the form of an infusion. Lovage leaves, fresh or dried, are used as a herb in cooking. The plant contains vitamin C.

Flax

Linum usitatissimum L.

Description: An annual or (rarely) biennial plant, 20–150 cm high with a thin rootstock and an erect, densely foliate stem, branched in its upper part. The leaves are narrow and pointed, up to 30 cm long. Five-petalled flowers grow on long petioles, flowering in June and July; they are light blue, rarely pink or white. The fruit is a globose capsule, usually with ten glossy, yellow-brown to red-brown seeds.

Origin and Distribution: A widely cultivated plant native to the temperate parts of Europe. Grows well in both warm and cold regions, at all altitudes. Grown throughout the whole of Europe, North America and Asia as far as the subtropical zone.

Cultivation and Preparation: The two basic groups of cultivated flax are the variety *vulgare,* grown for its fibres which are used in the textile industry, and the variety *humile,* grown mainly for its oily seeds. Recently, a variety yielding both fibres and seeds rich in oil has been introduced.

Constituents: Flax seeds contain up to 40 per cent oil rich in glycerides, linolenic acids (65 per cent), linoleic acid (25 per cent) and other unsaturated acids. They also contain 3–6 per cent mucilages and various other substances such as the poisonous hydrogen cyanate which is found only in the ground seeds.

Cosmetic Uses: Cold-pressed linseed oil forms a uniformly thin protective film on the skin. The complex of substances in it, known as vitamin F, heals rashes, burns, psoriasis and numerous other skin diseases. Linseed oil therefore forms part of medicinal and cosmetic preparations for inflamed skin. Nevertheless, sensitive skin may sometimes be irritated by linseed oil.

Other Uses: A decoction of the ripe seeds extracted with cold water yields mucilages which can be used as a mild laxative. However, flax is important mainly in the textile industry as a raw material from which the best-quality linen is made.

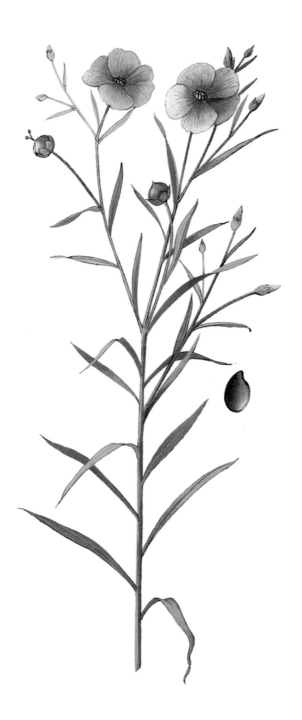

Oriental Sweet Gum

Liquidambar orientalis Mill.

Hamamelidaceae

Description: A robust deciduous tree more than 30 m high, with leaves resembling those of maple or plane on long petioles with stipules. The flowers are of two kinds, the male ones in erect, cylindrical, dense spikes, the female ones in globose clusters at the ends of long, leafless stalks. The fruit is a capsule formed at the same time as the flowers, and resembles a bristly ball. Each capsule contains one or two winged seeds.

Origin and Distribution: This species comes originally from Turkey, Syria and Iran but its cultivation has spread to many other countries.

Harvesting and Preparation: Injured trees exude a balsam called *Balsamum styrax,* or storax; healthy trees do not produce it. By injuring young wood receptacles secreting this balsam form in the trunk. Systematic and intentional injuring of the trunk (by beating or incision of the bark) results in these receptacles enlarging and joining up to form a system of canals in which storax is accumulated. Storax is obtained by boiling the peeled-off bark.

Constituents: Raw storax is purified and a syrupy, delicately aromatic substance containing styracine, cinnamates, vanillin and other substances is obtained.

Cosmetic Uses: The concentrated fragrant substance, or resinoid, is used to make perfumes used for soaps, powders, face creams, gels, lipsticks, hair lotions and shampoos. It is well-known as an excellent scent fixative. According to their place of origin several kinds of storax can be distinguished, all of which must be differentiated from the species *Styrax officinalis* which produces the resin *Resina benzoö* (benzoin, gum benzoin, benjamin gum). The resinoid of this drug, with a high content of vanillin, is also used in perfumery.

Other Uses: The fragrant wood of this tree is valuable timber. A related species — *Liquidambar styraciflua* from North America — yields sweet gum (copalm) used for chewing gum.

Tomato
Solanaceae

Lycopersicon esculentum Mill.
syn. *Solanum lycopersicum*

Description: An annual, fast-growing plant, with many branches, all covered with soft glandular hairs, which give off the characteristic tomato smell. Leaves are interruptedly unpaired pinnate bearing in their axils yellow star-like flowers arranged in clusters. The fruit is usually a multichambered, juicy berry, but in cultivated plants it greatly varies in shape, size and colour, and can be globose to irregularly lobate, smooth or deeply grooved, red, yellow or orange.

Origin and Distribution: Probably native to the mountain valleys of the Peruvian Andes from where it was introduced to Europe in the 16th century. During the 18th and 19th centuries its cultivation spread throughout the world and it became an important food plant. Related species *Solanum racemigerum* and *Solanum pimpinelifolium* are used for hybridization in the breeding of new varieties.

Constituents: The edible fruits contain organic acids, saccharides, carotenoid colouring substances, vitamins C, A and B complex, and inorganic substances. The rest of the plant is poisonous.

Cosmetic Uses: The juice of fresh tomatoes cleanses, refines and beautifies the skin. Tomatoes are therefore useful in fruit pulp face packs. To prepare a tomato pack, cut tomatoes into thin slices, squash them and mix with several drops of lemon juice. On a well-washed face apply a moisturizer in a thin film, then cover with a thin layer of dry cotton wool which is in turn covered with a layer of cotton wool soaked with the mashed tomato pulp. After a quarter of an hour the pack is removed, more moisturizer is applied to the face and cleaned off with cotton wool soaked in tomato juice. The pack is excellent for blackheads and faded, tired skin. Tomato juice is also added to face creams.

Other Uses: Tomatoes are a popular vegetable and are used in a wide variety of ways. Tomato juice is drunk, tomatoes may be eaten fresh or cooked, used to make juice or preserved as tomato purée, ketchup, and chutney.

142

Creeping Jenny

Primulaceae

Lysimachia nummularia L.

Description: A prostrate, trailing, perennial waterside plant, reaching 60 cm in height at most. The opposite, rounded leaves are about 25 mm in diameter and grow on short petioles. The solitary flowers rising from the leaf axils are yellow with dark dots, appearing from June to August. The fruit is a capsule with tiny seeds.

Origin and Distribution: Probably native to Europe from where it spread to the New World. The evergreen plants form a dense mat, and are therefore excellent as ground cover.

Harvesting and Preparation: The whole flowering herb is gathered and dried in shade.

Constituents: The flowering herb contains saponins, tannins and the ferment primaverase splitting glycoside bonds.

Cosmetic Uses: Recommended in baths for chronic eczema, as an infusion (100 g per litre of boiling water, extracted for about 30 minutes). The same infusion is suitable for washing the face in cases of acne and boils. The tannins in the infusion close open pores. They also help if an infusion is used as a hair rinse for greasy hair and dandruff.

Other Uses: Obsolete in European medicine and in folk medicine now largely neglected. In the past *Lysimachia* was used against diarrhoea, varicose veins and externally for the bathing of wounds. An infusion of leaves and flowers is occasionally drunk as a tea. Some related species are used in cooking *(Lysimachia clethroides, L. fortunei, L. obovata);* others may be chewed to refresh the breath (the roots of *L. foenum-grecum*).

Balm

Labiatae

Melissa officinalis L.

Description: A perennial plant of shrubby growth, reaching about 50 cm in height. Its numerous leaves are heart-shaped or ovoid, serrate, sparsely hairy. The flowers are small and white, appearing from June till July. Prefers sheltered, sunny places and rich soil. Propagated by seed or root division.

Distribution: The ancient Greeks and Romans were aware of the curative properties of balm which grew wild in southern Europe and central Asia. Balm was used by them as a condiment, as well as a medicinal and honey-bearing plant. Its name is derived from the Greek word *melissa,* meaning honey-bearing (melliferous). It is popular for its lemon-like scent and often grown in gardens.

Harvesting and Preparation: Plants 25 – 30 cm high or just the leaves of the plants are harvested before flowering. There can be up to three harvests a year. It must be gathered in dry weather, in the morning after the dew has dried, and dried quickly in shade (if dried slowly the leaves turn brown). It cannot be stored for long, as it rapidly loses its scent.

Constituents: This species has usually been called an essential-oil plant, although its volatile oil content is negligible. It is distilled from fresh plants with steam, and contains citral, citronelal, geraniol and linalool.

Cosmetic Uses: Balm is used in herbal mixtures for tonic baths and products for greasy skin and hair. It may be added in any amounts to herb packs of all kinds, to give the skin a pleasant, fresh scent. It also prevents headaches from which some people suffer after a herb pack application. Balm oil has an excellent scent, but is often replaced in perfumery by less expensive volatile oils such as those from various *Cymbopogon* species.

Other Uses: In pharmacy alcohol extracts of balm are used for the preparation of many popular remedies for headache, nervous problems, insomnia and hysteria (Carmelite water).

Peppermint

Labiatae

Mentha x *piperita* L.

Description: A perennial plant about 60 cm high, with hollow, quadrangular stems. The petiolate, ovoid-lanceolate leaves have prominent venation and diffuse a strong, characteristic menthol smell. Pale purple flowers in dense spikes appear from July to September. Propagation is vegetative – the plants form an underground network of woody shoots or runners. Various mint species hybridize naturally and peppermint is thought to be a hybrid of water mint *(Mentha aquatica)* and spearmint *(Mentha spicata)*.

Distribution: Peppermint is found wild around the Mediterranean and the eastern USA, and is widely cultivated throughout Europe, North America and the former USSR. There are numerous varieties of mint; all prefer warm, moist, sunny places and rich soil.

Harvesting and Preparation: Usually the whole herb is harvested, immediately before flowering, up to 3 times a year and dried quickly in shade at a temperature not exceeding 35° C.

Constituents: In all mint species volatile oil is the active substance. It is obtained commercially mainly from a hybrid cultivar originally bred in England and known as 'Mitcham'. It contains approximately 1 per cent volatile oil with about 50 per cent menthol, as well as menthon, phellandrene, pinene and cineole. The eastern Asian and Japanese cultivars, which have a much higher menthol content, are also a significant source of menthol produced industrially.

Cosmetic Uses: Menthol is an essential raw material in the production of toothpastes, mouthwashes, refreshing massage creams, bath additives, face packs and gels. It gives them a refreshing smell and has a cooling, soothing effect on contact with the skin. Demand for menthol is so great that enough cannot be supplied from natural sources, and so menthol is also produced synthetically. Another component of mint oil, menthon, is used in the perfume industry.

Other Uses: Mint oil and menthol are very important medicinally, for their disinfectant and soothing effects. They are used for the treatment of gastrointestinal difficulties and in the preparation of anti-rheumatic ointments.

Nutmeg

Myristica fragrans Houtt.

Description: An ornamental, tropical, evergreen tree with a conical dark green crown, up to 6–8 m in height. Male flowers are small, whitish, arranged in clusters, and female flowers are usually solitary, rising from the leaf axils; the tree blooms all year round. The fruit is a one-seeded berry, in shape like a peach with a somewhat pointed end. Ripe fruit is greenish-yellow with a red tinge, cracking along a groove from the top to the stem. The fruit pulp is rather thick, with a sour taste and the characteristic nutmeg smell. Inside it is a fleshy red membrane, the mace, covering the hard kernel, known as nutmeg.

Origin, Distribution and Harvesting: Nutmeg is native to Indonesia and cultivated in the West Indies and other tropical areas. The fruit is picked by hand or knocked off the trees with bamboo poles. Only dry, cracked fruit is harvested, then the pulp is removed and the mace separated carefully from the nutmeg with fingers or knife. Both are dried for several days in the sun.

Constituents: Nutmegs and mace *(Macis)* contain volatile oils of almost identical composition. The best − banda nutmegs − contain up to 16 per cent volatile oil, consisting of the terpenes α-pinene, camphene, limonene, p-cymene and alcohols (linalool, borneol, terpineol, geraniol). The volatile oil also contains the toxic and hallucinogenic chemical myristicin. Eating as few as two nutmegs can cause death. Nutmegs also contain 30−40 per cent fat (nutmeg butter) and 30 per cent starch.

Cosmetic Uses: Nutmeg oil is used mainly for perfuming soaps. It is also a constituent of some chypre-type perfumes.

Other Uses: Nutmeg and mace have long been used mainly as a seasoning in cooking.

Myrtle

Myrtaceae

Myrtus communis L.

Description: A bushy evergreen shrub about 3 m high, with small, narrow, glossy leaves smelling pleasantly when rubbed. Small, fragrant, white or pinkish flowers appear from June to August. The fruit is a small, hoary berry, green turning to purple-black.

Origin and Distribution: Myrtle comes from the Mediterranean region and was cultivated in the gardens of the ancient Greeks and Romans. It was consecrated to Aphrodite (Venus), the goddess of Love, and myrtle twigs were used to symbolize youth and beauty. In ancient Egypt women would wreathe their hair with lotus, pomegranate and myrtle twigs for dancing on festive occasions. Many different varieties are now cultivated.

Preparation: This species is the only myrtaceous plant rich in volatile oils in Europe. Myrtle oil is expressed from the whole plant or the leaves and is chiefly grown for this purpose in Spain, France, Corsica, Sicily and the northwestern coast of Africa.

Constituents: The volatile oil has a penetrating camphor-like smell and contains α-pinene, cineole, camphene, dipentene, geraniol, nerol, eugenol, limonene and tannins. It has a disinfectant effect.

Cosmetic Uses: Myrtle oil is used to aromatize toothpastes, mouthwashes, aftershaves (and men's cosmetics in general), massage creams and bath additives. As myrtle also contains a considerable quantity of tannins a myrtle bath is refreshing, promotes blood circulation to the skin and has disinfectant and deodorizing effects.

Other Uses: The dried green berries are sometimes used as a spice and may be chewed to refresh the breath. Myrtle wood is hard and dense, and is used for the carving of small tools and walking sticks. Myrtle is also grown as an ornamental shrub. In some countries it is the custom for wedding guests to adorn themselves with its green shoots.

Olive
Oleaceae

Olea europaea L.

Description: A subtropical evergreen tree, with a gnarled, greyish-green trunk, 7–12 m high. It has narrow, grey-green, leathery leaves and bears small whitish flowers arranged in axillary panicles. The fruit is an oblong yellowish-green, purple drupe containing a spindle-shaped hard stone.

Origin and Distribution: Native to the whole Mediterranean region where it is very common. Widely cultivated in dry subtropical regions of both the Old and New Worlds.

Cultivation and Harvesting: Olive trees are grown in plantations. Ripe olives are shaken from the trees and gathered, either to make olive oil, which is expressed at various pressures and temperatures (cold-pressed oil is the best), or to eat as a fruit.

Constituents: Olive oil is one of the best culinary oils, easily digested and with a distinctive taste. It is also one of the basic raw materials used in the cosmetics industry for the manufacture of the best-quality products. Cold-pressed olives yield 40–60 per cent oil, containing mainly glycerides of oleic acid (75 per cent) and glycerides of palmitic and linolenic acids. Under higher pressures and temperatures, oil of poorer quality with a higher percentage of free fatty acids is obtained.

Cosmetic Uses: Like almond and avocado oils, olive oil is used for cleansing sensitive skin and to protect dry and ageing skin, either in its natural state, without perfumes, or processed in face packs, rich creams, shampoos, foam baths and bath oils. The best lotions and creams made from natural oils for dry skin usually contain olive or sesame oils, and to a lesser extent avocado or peach kernel oils.

Other Uses: In pharmacopoeias olive oil is the current medium for drugs soluble in oil. It may be used internally for colic, to expel small gallstones and as a laxative. Olives as such are a popular fruit, eaten either unripe and green, variously preserved (in salt or vinegar) or ripe and black. Olive wood is very hard and dense and is used for woodcarving.

Ginseng

Araliaceae

Panax pseudoginseng Wall.

Description: A perennial plant about 30–70 cm high, sometimes living as long as 100 years. The fleshy yellow root is usually 20–25 cm long and about 2 cm in diameter, with two to six branches. The root shape sometimes resembles the human figure. From the root rises a simple stem bearing near the top a rosette of three to five palmately compound petiolate leaves. The stem and petioles are reddish-violet. From the rosette the stem continues as a flower stalk terminating in an umbel of greenish-white inconspicuous flowers which appear in July. The fruits are bright red berries ripening in August and September, the most suitable time for harvesting the root.

Distribution: Ginseng occurs wild in the Far East in the USSR, China and Korea, and is cultivated mainly in the former USSR, Japan, Korea and China. It grows in the depths of mountain forests, mostly in mixed cedar-deciduous woodland. To the ginseng root a legendary, miraculous medicinal power has been ascribed; it is used mainly in eastern Asia. The wild plant is very rare and its cultivation is difficult.

Constituents: Only the roots are used. Their active substances are not fully known, but they have been used as a panacea for all ailments for thousands of years.

Cosmetic Uses: Dried root extracts are added to various nutritious creams, face lotions and packs, for their alleged rejuvenating effects which result in improved appearance. The effects of ginseng, when applied externally, have not been scientifically confirmed, but the drug is undoubtedly harmless, if not beneficial, when used cosmetically.

Other Uses: Internally administered, ginseng root has stimulant and rejuvenating effects and this is why it is added to numerous remedies promoting mental and physical vigour. Considered very important in east Asian medicine, its use in Europe and America has become fashionable rather than a necessity.

Geranium

Geraniaceae

Pelargonium odoratissimum (L.) Ait.

Description: A perennial plant up to 1 m high, with large, pinnate, deeply lobed leaves covered with glandular hairs, on long petioles. It has a strong, pleasant smell. The flowers, in dense umbels, have five sepals, the rear sepal merging with the pedicel to form a narrow spur. The five-petalled corolla is pink and symmetrical. From the ovary ripens the fruit resembling a straight bill.

Origin and Distribution: Native to south Africa but cultivated in the whole of Africa, especially in Algeria, and in southern Europe, mainly in Spain, France, Corsica and Turkey. The plant requires a sunny, well-drained spot and is easily propagated by stem cuttings. Grown as a house plant or as a tender annual in cooler regions.

Harvesting and Processing: Whole plants are harvested before the flower buds open, and the volatile oil is distilled from them immediately. The species *Pelargonium roseum* and *Pelargonium graveolens* are as important commercially.

Constituents: The fragrant geraniol oil is contained mainly in the glandular hairs on the leaves. It is obtained by distillation with steam, yielding $0.1-0.2$ per cent oil, the main components of which are geraniol and citronellol.

Cosmetic Uses: Geraniol oil is an important ingredient in cosmetics. Annual consumption amounts to approximately 130,000 kg worldwide. It forms part of the rose-type perfumes, used in mouthwashes, creams, face milks and lotions, soaps, lipsticks, powders, oils, brilliantines and bath additives. Pure geraniol is used in the same way as geraniol oil.

Other Uses: Numerous species, hybrids and varieties of geranium are grown as decorative plants, for their profuse and showy flowers. They are easy to grow and propagate.

158

Avocado Pear

Persea americana Mill.

Lauraceae

Description: An evergreen subtropical or tropical tree 6−20 m high, with a crown varying in shape from narrow and pyramidal to broadly branched. It has thick branches, the young ones olive green, fragile, becoming grey-brown. The smooth glossy leaves are ovoid with a distinct point, 5−30 cm long. Tiny yellow-green flowers are arranged in compact clusters of 200−300 flowers in the leaf axils. The fruit is a large, fleshy berry, usually pear-shaped, 7−20 cm long, with either a yellowish-green, dark green, brownish or dark purple skin. Inside is a single large seed surrounded by a yellow, moderately sweet pulp of a solid butter consistency, nutty taste and pleasant smell.

Origin and Distribution: Native to Central America where, long before the discovery of the New World, it served the Indians as a nutritious source of food, rich in calories and fat. Now extensively cultivated all over America, Africa and Israel.

Constituents: The fruit, especially its fleshy part, contains up to 30 per cent non-drying oil of high quality, consisting of glycerides of oleic, palmitic and linoleic acids.

Cosmetic Uses: Intensive cultivation on the American continent fostered the use of avocado oil in various cosmetics of American make. It appears as a part of various lotions, bath oils for dry skin and moisturizers. Avocado oil is excellent as a hot face pack for rough, dry skin: the face is covered with a very thin layer of cotton wool saturated with warm avocado oil. The face is covered with a cloth, to prevent rapid cooling of the oil which is left on the skin for 20 minutes. After removing the pack the face is wiped with a soft dry towel. (Olive and almond oils are equally suitable for hot face packs.)

Other Uses: Avocados are eaten as a fruit (their calorific value is twice that of bananas) in a variety of ways: cold with a dressing, in salads and with other vegetables; and hot, in soups and sauces. They are also dried and ground into flour.

160

Hamburg Parsley

Umbelliferae

Petroselinum crispum ssp. *tuberosum* (Bernh. et Rehb.)

Description: A biennial plant, forming in its first year a rosette of basal leaves from which rises in the second year the flower-bearing, hollow stem, branched in its upper part, up to 1 m high. The thick tapering root is usually simple or sparsely branched, and spindle shaped. The fruit is a small greenish-brown achene. The leaves, like those of other wild parsleys, are segmented, with a triangular outline; there are many cultivated parsleys with deeply divided, curly leaves.

Origin and Distribution: Parsley is native to the Mediterranean region, where it usually grows in rocky places near water. Now distributed throughout Europe where it was introduced by the Romans, and widely grown all over the world.

Harvesting and Preparation: The root is harvested in the autumn or spring of the second year. After being thoroughly washed it is dried or stored in a cold place, preferably in sand. The fruit is harvested in the second year in August, and the leaves are gathered in July and August.

Constituents: All parts of the plant contain volatile oil of varying composition according to its place of origin. They can contain myristicine, apiol or allyltetramethoxybenzol. The roots contain $0.1-0.3$ per cent, and the fruit $2-6$ per cent volatile oil. The leaves are also rich in vitamin C.

Cosmetic Uses: In cases of excessive perspiration and greasy skin prone to pimples a parsley infusion (10 g of root to 100 g of water) is recommended (drink one cup three times a day, twice a week). It helps to eliminate waste from the body, thus cleansing the skin. The grated root or leaves should not, however, be used in face packs, as the volatile oil causes inflammation, swelling and rashes if it comes in direct contact with the skin. A small quantity of parsley oil or the fresh leaves can be added to herbal bath mixtures.

Other Uses: Parsley is an invaluable diuretic and also has anti-rheumatic and dehydrating effects. Hamburg parsley is used as root vegetable, while the leaves of other varieties are widely used as a seasoning.

162

Bayberry, Pimento

Myrtaceae

Pimenta racemosa (Mill.) J. W. Moore
syn. *Pimenta acris* (Sw.) Lindl.

Description: A small tropical evergreen tree up to 7 m high, with leathery leaves on short petioles, which diffuse a pleasant smell when rubbed. The inconspicuous flowers are arranged in loose clusters. The fruits are small round berries, first green, later black.

Origin and Distribution: Native to the Caribbean countries and Central America. It is sometimes cultivated but usually wild trees are utilized.

Harvesting and Preparation: The leaves, the most valuable part, are harvested the third year after planting. They are dried in the sun before being sent to factories for further processing. From 100 kg of dry leaves about 1,100 g of volatile oil are obtained. The immature fruit is also harvested and used as a substitute for the fruit of the closely related allspice tree *Pimenta dioica* – allspice, pimento.

Constituents: The fruit and leaves of both species contain volatile oil (3–5 per cent) with 80 per cent eugenol, cineole, phellandrene and caryophyllene. The volatile oil is obtained from the unripe fruit (ripe fruit contains less) and leaves by distillation with steam. In the past volatile oil from the leaves was distilled with a mixture of rum and water to make bay rum, used as a perfume (mainly for the hair) or toilet water.

Cosmetic Uses: The disinfectant and deodorant properties of eugenol in the volatile oil are utilized in toothpastes, mouthwashes and soaps. However, it is not very important and its use is limited.

Other Uses: The fruit of both species is important in cookery as a spice. One of the hottest kinds of spice, the so-called 'Mexico-Piment' or 'Tabasco-Piment', comes from *Pimenta dioica* var. *tabasco*. It contains about 1 per cent volatile oil.

Scots Pine
Pinus silvestris L.

Pinaceae

Description: A coniferous tree up to 30 m high, with a smooth red bark. The outer bark of the trunk is cracked at the base. The young branches are greyish-yellow, and bear pairs of stiff, twisted, bluish or greyish-green needle-shaped leaves. Clusters of male flowers in spikes form on the base of new offshoots; the solitary female flowers rise under the apical bud of the leading shoot, and form cones; after pollination winged seeds develop.

Distribution: The species is common in Europe and Asia. It tolerates dry, sandy soils and this is why it is cultivated chiefly in places where other coniferous trees cannot be easily grown.

Preparation: Oil of turpentine from pine needles and pine wood, and lightwood oil from the wood are obtained by distillation with steam. The tree trunk exudes terpentine balsam, a sticky mixture of volatile oil and resin that solidifies on contact with air.

Constituents: Oil of turpentine differs according to species and the parts of the tree from which it is obtained. There are at least three kinds; the volatile oil from the needles and immature cones of *Pinus silvestris* contains α-pinene, limonene, dipentene and camphene.

Cosmetic Uses: Pinenes are important cosmetically, as the basic ingredient used to produce many scents. Oil of turpentine or decoctions of pine needles also form part of most bath additives, because they have disinfectant, refreshing and deodorant effects, and a beneficial effect on blood circulation. They can, however, cause an allergic reaction in very sensitive skin.

Other Uses: Firm and durable pinewood is widely used in the manufacture of furniture. It is also used in the production of cellulose and tar.

Ribwort Plantain

Plantaginaceae

Plantago lanceolata L.

Description: A perennial plant with a short, vertical rootstock; from it rises a basal rosette of long, lanceolate, often hairy leaves with parallel veins, narrowed to form a long petiole. Several leafless stems longer than the leaves (10−50 cm high) rise from the leaf rosette, and terminate in a short, cylindrical spike composed of tiny, yellowish-white flowers and brown bracts. Plantain flowers from May till September. The fruit is an ovoid capsule containing two relatively large seeds.

Distribution: The plant is abundant in Europe, North America and Asia, in meadows, roadsides, field paths, banks, ditches and deciduous woodland; it is a common weed in gardens and fields, particularly clover fields.

Harvesting and Preparation: The leaves should be gathered from May to August, from non-flowering plants, and dried in thin layers in shade to prevent them losing their green colour.

Constituents: The drug contains mucilages, tannins and the glycoside aucubine. These substances act together as an astringent and expectorant.

Cosmetic Uses: An infusion (50 g of leaves to half a litre of warm water, extracted for 30 minutes) mixed with an equal amount of diluted alcohol makes an excellent skin lotion for greasy skin and acne. The crushed fresh leaves can be used in herbal face packs. Freshly expressed juice from the leaves can be added to face creams for greasy, inflamed skin. The seeds of a Mediterranean species *Plantago psyllium,* which contain up to 10 per cent mucilages, can be made into an infusion with cold water, and used in nourishing skin creams and lotions.

Other Uses: Plantain leaves are considered very effective medicinally, for internal and external use. Internally they are made into in syrups, drops and teas for inflammations of the upper respiratory tract, coughs, catarrhs and as an intestinal regulator. Externally, a decoction or a poultice of fresh, well-washed, crushed leaves is recommended for application to wounds which then heal more quickly, and to insect bites, to reduce the swelling and itching.

Patchouli

Labiatae

Pogostemon cablin (Blanco) Benth.
syn. *Pogostemon patchouli* Pellet.

Description: A tropical evergreen shrub about 120 cm high. It has broad leaves on long petioles and white flowers. It rarely forms seeds, and so must be propagated by means of axial cuttings.

Origin and Distribution: Native to India, Burma, Malaysia and the Philippines. Now cultivated mainly in Sumatra, the Seychelles, Madagascar and Brazil.

Harvesting and Preparation: Plantations of patchouli are set up with the plants in rows 90 cm apart. Harvesting begins about six months after planting and continues at intervals of four to six months. The young parts of the plants are cut, dried in the sun and sent to factories for processing. In China the leaves are first stacked and left to ferment. On average, 1.5 tons of dried leaves are harvested per hectare.

Constituents: The leaves smell somewhat like sandalwood or musk. Its woody, camphor-like scent derives from the volatile oil, whose individual components vary according to its place of origin, but which are mainly benzaldehyde, eugenol, cinnamalaldehyde, azulene, quajene and patchulene.

Cosmetic Uses: The resinoid patchouli, obtained by extraction from the dried fermented leaves, is an excellent scent fixative, adding freshness to perfumes and increasing the perception of their other scents. The volatile oil or resinoid is used to perfume cosmetics such as soaps. Today, of course, many synthetic musks are used instead, being cheaper to produce.

Other Uses: Patchouli leaves make an excellent insecticide and are put with clothes in wardrobes as a moth repellent. The covers of Kashmir shawls exported to Europe are soaked in patchouli oil for this purpose.

Tuberose

Agavaceae

Polianthes tuberosa L.

Description: A perennial plant with a solid, pulpy, bulbous tuber. A tuft of grasslike leaves grows at ground level; from it rises a robust stem (sometimes two or three stems) about 50 cm high, with alternate, linear leaves. The stems terminate in a spike of waxy flowers, white or creamy to pinkish, with six open petals growing from a funnel-shaped tube. The flowers diffuse a characteristic penetrating fragrance.

Origin and Distribution: The plant comes from Mexico where it grows on dry, bare slopes up to 2,500 m above sea level. In southern Europe and northern Africa it is cultivated in the open, but in cooler climates it is grown as a greenhouse pot plant.

Constituents: The part of the plant used is its fragrant flowers from which a small quantity (0.08 per cent) of volatile oil is obtained. This oil contains methylester of benzoic acid, benzylalcohol and benzylbenzoate.

Cosmetic Uses: From the volatile oil tuberose perfume is manufactured; it was very popular in the past, but is less so today. It is manufactured mainly in southern France, Spain and Egypt and used to perfume some cosmetics such as creams, skin lotions, lipsticks and powders.

Other Uses: In the past the beautiful, fragrant tuberose was very popular as a cut flower, but is not often seen today.

172

Water Pepper

Polygonum hydropiper L.

Description: An annual plant with a branching stem up to 1 m high. Where it branches the stem is often swollen, with a reddish tinge. The dark green leaves are linear-lanceolate with transparent dots. The plant bears small, greenish or pinkish flowers arranged in drooping clusters, appearing from June to September. The fruit is a tiny achene.

Distribution: Found in Europe, Asia and North America. Abundant in moist, shady places, on bare soil, mainly on flooded river banks, damp forests, and near ponds and lakes.

Harvesting and Preparation: The herb is cut during flowering and dried in shade, at a temperature not exceeding 40° C. The plant is odourless but has an acrid taste. When dried, the amount of active substances considerably decreases so it is better to use fresh plants.

Constituents: The acrid, pepper-like taste which gave the species its common name is caused by the ketonealdehyde tadeonal. It also contains flavonides and tannins with astringent properties, vitamins A and C and the antihaemorrhagic vitamin K. Water pepper is not the only species used in cosmetics and medicine. The genus *Polygonum* comprises about 150 species. *Polygonum aviculare* (knotgrass), containing tannins, silicic acid and mucilage, and *Polygonum bistorta* (bistort), rich in tannins (20 per cent), especially in its rootstock, have a similar effect.

Cosmetic Uses: Infusion or decoction of the herb (20−30 g to 100 ml of water) are used as an astringent for the skin, to close the pores, and tighten the skin. As a bath additive they have tonic and sedative effects.

Other Uses: All the above species as well as some others are used for coughs and colds and for intestinal problems including bloody diarrhoea.

Cowslip

Primulaceae

Primula veris L.

Description: A perennial plant up to 30 cm high, with a short, cylindrical rhizome and numerous rootlets. The leaves are ovoid, crenate, downy on the reverse, with prominent veins. The finely hairy stem bears a simple umbel of flowers on long pedicels, with a tubular, yellowish-green calyx and yellow, tubular petals, extended in their upper part. The plant flowers from April to May. The fruit is a capsule.

Distribution: Native to Europe and Asia, where it grows in sunny, damp meadows, forest clearings and deciduous woodland.

Harvesting and Preparation: The flowers and rhizomes with their roots can be used, but because the plant is becoming rare and must be protected, only cultivated plants should be gathered. The flowers are gathered in April and May and the rootstocks in spring, before growth starts. Both parts of the plant are dried in shade or in the sun, in a temperature not exceeding 40° C. The dried flowers smell slightly of honey, the rhizomes of anise. Fresh roots are odourless.

Constituents: The flowers contain saponins (only 2 per cent), the glycosides primaverine, primulaverine and a small quantity of volatile oil (0.01 per cent).

Cosmetic Uses: Cowslips are not often used cosmetically, as the content of saponins, the main active substance, is low in the flowers, and the roots, which contain more saponins (10 per cent), should not be gathered. Saponins can in any case be obtained from other sources. Nevertheless, an infusion of the flowers (10 g to 100 g boiling water) may be used as a hair rinse, to make the hair shiny, soft and slightly fragrant. An infusion is also good for washing greasy skin with clogged pores.

Other Uses: For inflammations of the upper respiratory tract, a cowslip decoction may be used as an expectorant. The species *Primula elatior* can be used in the same way; although it does not contain volatile oil its effects are the same.

Almond

Rosaceae

Prunus dulcis (Mill.) D. A. Webb.
syn. *Amygdalus dulcis* L.

Description: A subtropical deciduous tree up to 5−8 m high. The crowns of young trees are usually erect, spreading in older trees. The lanceolate leaves are dark green and finely serrate. The flowers grow in pairs on two-year-old wood, and are deep pink in sweet varieties, and white to pinkish in bitter varieties. The flowers appear in early spring, before the leaves. The fruit is an ovoid drupe, the so-called almond; it has a grey-green, tomentose pericarp, containing a single stone with one, rarely more, flattened seeds, the edible kernels.

Origin and Distribution: Native to Asia Minor, and cultivated round the Mediterranean and throughout the warm regions of the temperate zone.

Constituents: The main active component, cosmetically and pharmaceutically, is almond oil, the most expensive non-drying oil. It consists mostly of glycerides of oleic and linoleic acids, and the amount varies between 40 and 55 per cent. The oil is cold-pressed, usually from bitter almonds, as sweet almonds are scarcer and therefore too expensive for this purpose. The toxin hydrogen cyanate, released from the amygdaline in bitter almonds, does not pass into the oil, but remains in the compact press-cake which is then discarded in most cases. The press-cake from sweet almonds does not contain amygdaline and is used as a raw material in the manufacture of cosmetics.

Cosmetic Uses: Almond oil does not irritate the skin and is therefore useful for the cleansing of sensitive skin and as an emollient for dry skin. It forms part of the best cosmetic lotions, milks and creams. The ground press-cake yields almond bran, also used for cleansing very sensitive skin. The bran is diluted with lukewarm water to make a thick paste, applied to the face and washed off after 10 minutes with more lukewarm water. Almond bran can also be mixed with barley or oat bran.

Other Uses: Sweet almonds make delicious eating, either fresh or roasted and salted, and large amounts are also used to make cakes and also confectionery. Bitter almonds (persicoes) are sometimes added in small quantities to confectionery, where they impart their own particular smell and flavour.

Peach

Rosaceae

Prunus persica (L.) Batch.

Description: A subtropical, deciduous shrub or small tree reaching approximately 5 m in height. The leaves are long and narrow, serrate, smelling of bitter almonds when rubbed. It has showy, white, pinkish or deep pink, sessile flowers which appear in early spring, before the leaves. The fruit is a globose, fleshy drupe, up to 14 cm in diameter, with a soft downy surface, orange-yellow with red or purplish tinges, and sweet, juicy flesh.

Origin and Distribution: Unknown in the wild, but widely cultivated as an orchard tree, originally only in China and later in warm regions throughout the temperate zone.

Cultivation and Harvesting: Peach trees are cultivated commercially in plantations; the fruit ripens from the beginning of July till September, but mostly at the end of August, depending on the variety. Numerous hybrids have been developed, varying in growth, time of ripening, taste and juiciness. The fruit is picked by hand and cannot be stored for long.

Constituents: Peach (and apricot) pulp contains organic acids, sugars, vitamins and traces of elements which are interesting cosmetically. Peach oil expressed from the kernels contains glycerides of oleic and linoleic acids, similar to those of the almond oil.

Cosmetic Uses: The cosmetic industry makes use of various fruit pulps, including peach pulp, for products intended to tighten and refresh the skin, cleanse and contract the pores, smoothe wrinkles, and generally to improve the complexion. Peach oil is a raw material in the manufacture of creams, skin milks, facial massage oils, bath oils, skin lotions, hair softeners, and soaps. Along with almond and avocado oils, peach oil is used with vitamin complexes and fruit juices to make some of the best and most expensive cosmetics with regenerating and tonic effects.

Other Uses: Peaches are a well-known and popular fruit, eaten fresh and preserved.

Radish

Cruciferae

Raphanus sativus L.

Description: An annual to biennial plant with a tuberous taproot of varied shape and colour. The leaves are mostly broadly lyrate, and the flowers are white or pale lilac with violet veins, appearing from June to August. The swollen, ovoid-oblong fruit contains light brown seeds which are either almost spherical or of irregular shape.

Origin and Distribution: The species has two basic varieties: var. *major* (white radish) and var. *radicula* (garden radish). Both are old cultivated plants, probably of Asian origin, now widely grown in all countries of the temperate zone in many varieties differing in growth period, shape and colour. From the cosmetic point of view, black radish – *Raphanus sativus* var. *niger* is of most interest.

Cultivation and Harvesting: Either the fresh root or its juice is used. All white radish and garden radish varieties can be easily hybridized to form new cultivars.

Constituents: Black radish contains mustard oils in its roots. These volatile oils contain organically bound sulphur, the smell of which appears only after the plant tissue is damaged. It is caused by the reaction of mustard glycosides with the ferment myrosinase, which forms a substance that makes an excellent disinfectant. Also significant are the vitamin C content and trace elements.

Cosmetic Uses: Radish juice is good for treating greasy hair and dandruff, because of the content of organic sulphur compounds and mineral salts.

Other Uses: Radish is an excellent vegetable, used mainly in salads. Black radish juice is used medicinally for gall bladder and kidney difficulties and disorders of the digestive tract.

Pontic Rhubarb

Polygonaceae

Rheum rhabarbarum L.

Description: A robust perennial plant with a massive yellow rootstock and grooved, flower-bearing stems up to 2 m high and 3–5 cm thick. It has tough, ovoid to ovoid-triangular leaves with long, thick, smooth, pulpy petioles. From the end of May to June massive panicles of tiny whitish to yellowish flowers appear. The fruit is a winged achene.

Origin and Distribution: The numerous cultivated species probably developed from the wild rhubarb species native to eastern Siberia and northern Mongolia. *Rheum palmatum* and *Rheum officinale,* important in cosmetics and medicine, grow wild in the mountains of western China and Tibet.

Harvesting and Preparation: The part of the plant used as a drug is the massive rootstock. It was recommended in Chinese medicine as early as 2700 BC. It is used either powdered or in the form of extracts.

Constituents: The quality of the drug depends on its place of origin. The best is 'Shensi'; others are 'Szechwan', 'Canton', 'Shanghai', 'Tientsin' and 'Common round'. The drug contains cathartic glycosides (3–8 per cent), tannins and yellow pigments.

Cosmetic Uses: Most natural laxatives recommended for weight reduction contain active substances from rhubarb. Sometimes pure powdered rhubarb is administered, in 2–3 g doses a day. The drug is also used for hair colouring. To achieve a blond tint, 150 g of rhubarb root is boiled in half a litre of white wine until half the liquid has evaporated. The resulting concentrate is rubbed into the hair and left to dry.

Other Uses: Garden rhubarb species are grown for their massive red leaf-stalks which are eaten as a vegetable in puddings, or used to make marmalade. Rhubarb was first grown as a vegetable in England in the 18th century; from there its cultivation spread throughout Europe.

Castor-oil Plant

Ricinus communis L.

Euphorbiaceae

Description: An annual plant in the temperate zone, in the tropics a branched shrub or tree. The hollow stem is 1−2 m high, becoming woody with age, and is green, red or violet, usually waxy. The leaves are large, palmately lobed, with veins usually the same colour as the stem. Male and female flowers are arranged in racemes. The fruit is a capsule, usually spiny, containing smooth, oblong, black or mottled seeds with a fleshy excrescence.

Origin and Distribution: Probably native to western Africa or tropical Asia, and naturalized in the subtropics. Cultivated as an annual plant in the warm regions of the temperate zone. Grown for its oily seeds.

Constituents: The oil (55 per cent), important for cosmetic purposes, is expressed from the seeds by cold pressing, then boiled to remove the poisonous albumin ricin. The oil contains more than 85 per cent glycerides of ricinoleic acid and is soluble in ethanol.

Cosmetic Uses: The oil is added to cosmetics containing alcohol, such as face lotions and liquid brilliantines (hair oils combined with alcohol). A simple liquid brilliantine may be an emulsion of 10−50 per cent castor oil in 90 per cent alcohol, with a perfume. (Solid brilliantines are not manufactured from castor oil but from vaseline, lanolin and resins). Castor oil is also very good for dry skin.

Other Uses: Medicinally, castor oil is used as a laxative. Technically, castor oil is used as a lubricant for high-speed motors.

Cabbage Rose

Rosaceae

Rosa centifolia L.

Description: A perennial shrub up to 3 m high, with thorny brown branches. The leaves are unpaired pinnate, with ovoid, serrate leaflets. The pink flowers have a dense, full corolla diffusing a delicate, unobtrusive scent, and appear in summer. The fruit are tiny, hairy achenes enclosed in a fruit-like hip.

Origin and Distribution: Native to the Caucasian region and Iran; there are so many rose species and varieties, however, that it is sometimes difficult to determine their origin with certainty. Cabbage roses are one of the oldest of cultivated roses, and were widely grown in country gardens throughout the whole of Europe. Today they are cultivated in southern France, as the source of commercial rose water.

Harvesting and Preparation: For cosmetic, medicinal and culinary purposes the petals are gathered in dry weather in June and July, used either fresh for the manufacture of rose oil or dried quickly in shade. Dried petals must be kept in closed containers.

Constituents: *Rosa centifolia* is the raw material for French rose oil and rose water. Rose oil is obtained by extraction with volatile organic solvents, and contains mainly citronellol and geraniol. Dried petals contain traces of volatile oil, flavones and anthocyans and 10−25 per cent tannins of unknown composition.

Cosmetic Uses: An infusion or decoction of the flowers is recommended as a bath additive, mainly for damaged skin, to aid the healing of scars caused by pimples or minor injuries. Rose oil is used to perfume the best cosmetics and as a perfume by itself. Rose water, a by-product in the manufacture of rose oil, is also used in perfumery.

French Rose

Rosaceae

Rosa gallica L.

Description: A perennial climbing shrub 60−100 cm high, with trailing stems and erect thorny twigs bearing single, deep pink or red flowers. The thorny leaves are unpaired pinnate, consisting of five to seven leaflets, on long petioles. The strongly scented flowers appear in May and June. After the flowering period, hips enclosing hairy achenes are formed on the twigs.

Origin and Distribution: This species grows wild in Europe and western Asia, on chalky soils in woodland clearings. It is cultivated in France, Bulgaria, Greece, Turkey and the former USSR, for the fragrant rose oil. The closely related damask rose *(Rosa damascena),* in its red-flowering form *trigintipetala,* is the source of Bulgarian rose oil or attar of roses. It is cultivated in the famous 'Rose Valley' near Kazanlak in Bulgaria.

Harvesting and Preparation: The petals from which the volatile oil is distilled are gathered in full bloom, in the early morning when the content of volatile oil is at its highest. Production is enormous: approximately 4−5,000 kg of rose petals are harvested per hectare; from them about 1 kg of volatile oil is obtained.

Constituents: The content of volatile oil obtained by distillation with steam varies between 0.1−0.6 per cent. Its main components are citronellol (40−50 per cent) and geraniol (20 per cent).

Cosmetic Uses: The outstanding fragrance of the volatile oil makes it an invaluable perfume used in many cosmetics. Rose oil is suitable for making into face creams, lipsticks, skin lotions and powders. It is the basic substance for rose perfumes, it is used as a nuancer for 'Chat Noir', and is an active substance of Chanel No. 5 and Amber. Rose oil is very expensive and so it is frequently adulterated, often with palmarose oil obtained from Indian grass *(Cymbopogon martini)* or with volatile oils of some of the fragrant *Geranium* species.

Other Uses: In pharmacy, rose oil *(Oleum rosae)* and rose water *(Aqua rosae)* are used to perfume medicated creams and solutions for external use.

Rosemary

Rosmarinus officinalis L.

Labiatae

Description: A perennial, evergreen shrub 75−200 cm high, with twiggy branches and linear, leathery leaves which are dark green above and downy grey on the reverse. The pale violet to pale blue flowers rise from the leaf axils and flower from June to August.

Distribution: Rosemary grows wild in the Mediterranean region, and is cultivated in the rest of Europe, especially in Italy, Greece, Spain and Portugal. It requires protected, dry, sunny habitats, and grows well in humus-rich soil. It is propagated by cuttings of non-flowering shoots about 15 cm long, obtained from older plants.

Harvesting and Preparation: The herb is harvested and used fresh or dried in the shade. The drug has a camphor-like, spicy odour and a pungent, aromatic taste.

Constituents: The active substance is the volatile oil (1.5−2.5 per cent) containing cineole (30 per cent), borneol, bornylacetate, camphor, limonene and other components. The herb also contains tannins (10 per cent), flavonides and bitter substances.

Cosmetic Uses: Rosemary is used with other plant extracts for refreshing, disinfectant tonic baths and in herb mixtures for the hair. Rosemary extract or oil is used for perfuming soaps, aftershaves, face lotions and shampoos and as a component of some refreshing perfumes. It is not recommended for face packs, as it can cause irritation, swellings and rashes with prolonged use.

Other Uses: Rosemary has long been an important drug in folk medicine; the subject of many legends, it is highly esteemed in folk customs. According to one legend, the Virgin Mary spread her mantle on a rosemary shrub while resting during the flight of the Holy Family to Egypt, and the originally white flowers turned sky blue in Her honour. Excessive amounts of rosemary can cause poisoning, so it is usually used only externally, in ointments for rheumatism, sores and bruises. It may also be used as an insect repellent against moths.

White Willow

Salicaceae

Salix alba L.

Description: A deciduous tree up to 20 m high, with somewhat drooping branches. The bark of young branches is yellowish, turning brown later. The lanceolate leaves are ash-grey. Inconspicuous greenish female flowers (catkins) appear at the same time as the leaves. The ovary ripens into a capsule with tiny seeds with white downy tufts. The male flowers (on separate trees) are silky catkins that turn yellow with pollen.

Origin and Distribution: Indigenous to moist woodland and watersides in Europe and the cool regions of Asia. Introduced to North America.

Constituents: This and other willow trees, such as *Salix fragilis* and *Salix purpurea,* contain in their bark up to 10 per cent active phenylglycosides, tannins, flavone glycosides (isosalipurposide), compound derivatives of the glycoside salicin (e.g. populin, fragilin) and other substances. Before the closely related acetylsalicylic acid (Aspirin) was synthesized, willow bark was the source of salicin, from which salicylic acid, with its fever-reducing and anti-rheumatic effects, is formed in the body.

Cosmetic Uses: Willow bark decoction, containing tannins and salicylic compound, is used externally as an antiseptic and astringent. It is good for very greasy skin with open pores and pimples. Salicylic derivatives are extremely important in dermatology, as they are toxic to the fungi that cause skin diseases. This is why a willow bark decoction (100 g boiled for 15 minutes in a litre of water) is used, under medical supervision, in baths to treat fungally affected skin, along with salicylic and other ointments.

Other Uses: Willow wood is soft, pliable and easy to work, and is used in the manufacture of clogs (in the Netherlands), cricket bats, chests, frames for nets and other purposes. Young branches (osiers) are used for making baskets and garden furniture.

Garden Sage
Salvia officinalis L.

Labiatae

Description: A perennial sub-shrub, usually 50 cm but sometimes up to 1 m high. The upper parts of the stems are herbaceous, the lower parts woody. The downy leaves are petiolate, oblong-ovoid, with a finely wrinkled surface, and usually greenish to silver-grey. The flowers, arranged in false whorls, are violet, white or pink, flowering in June and July. The whole plant has a pleasant smell.

Origin and Distribution: Native to the Mediterranean region, and cultivated elsewhere in Europe and North America. Often grown in gardens, rarely escaping into the wild.

Harvesting and Preparation: Sage should be harvested shortly before it flowers, in dry weather, preferably at noon. The whole herb is gathered and dried as quickly as possible in shade, or artificially at temperatures up to 40° C. After drying the leaves are rubbed off the stalks.

Constituents: A fresh-smelling volatile oil (1−2.5 per cent) is distilled from the leaves. The composition of the oil varies according to its place of origin. Yugoslavian sage oil is considered the best; it contains 40 per cent thujone, 14 per cent cineole and about 20 per cent camphor. Spanish sage oils do not contain thujone but they have more cineole and camphor.

Cosmetic Uses: Because of its disinfectant, soothing, astringent and anti-inflammatory effects, sage oil is added to toothpastes and mouthwashes, anti-perspirant sprays, face lotions, soaps, shampoos and bath additives. The dried or fresh leaves can be used in the form of an infusion (100 g per litre of boiling water) as a hair rinse or for refreshing baths. Besides the volatile oil, the other sage constituents have a favourable effect, acting as an astringent and antibiotic.

Other Uses: Medicinally sage tea is used internally for indigestion, inflammations of the upper respiratory tract and as a gargle for a sore throat or mouth. Flowering sage is an important melliferous plant: sage honey is very flavoursome and highly valued. Sage is also used in cooking, particularly for meat dishes such as pork or game.

Elder

Caprifoliaceae

Sambucus nigra L.

Description: A shrub or tree up to 8 m high, with light greyish-brown, vertically cracked bark. The branches are greyish-white, with white pith inside. The leaves are unpaired pinnate, with oblong-ovoid, serrate leaflets. The creamy-white flowers, arranged in dense flat clusters, appear from the end of May till July; they give off an intense, sweetish smell. The fruit are round, glossy, violet-black berries containing a large quantity of dark juice.

Distribution: This species is found throughout Europe and Asia Minor, in moist, shady places such as deciduous and coniferous woodland, watersides and waste places. It prefers soils rich in nitrogen.

Harvesting and Preparation: Cosmetically, the flowers are used. (In folk medicine the bark, shoots and fruit are also used.) The flower clusters should be dried quickly in thin layers to preserve their colour; if dried slowly they turn brown and lose their value. Ripe fruit is gathered in autumn and consumed fresh (but always cooked) or dried.

Constituents: The active substances in the flowers are little-known glycosidically bound compounds, traces of volatile oil, mucilages, tannins, organic acids and vitamin C. In the fruit anthocyane colouring substances and phytoncidal antibacterial components are also found.

Cosmetic Uses: An infusion (two handfuls of flowers to a litre of boiling water, extracted until cool) may be used for washing problem skin and inflammations. It is added to the bath water for its tonic, sedative and stimulating effects. Apply in weekly cures with a week between each cure for about two months, preferably in summer. A face pack made from elder, linden and chamomile flowers is recommended for softening, clearing and toning the skin. Put the dried flowers of these three species in equal amounts into a porcelain bowl and mix with boiling water to make a paste. Wrap the mixture in a gauze cloth and apply to the clean face, pressing it gently to the contours of the skin. After 20 minutes the pack is washed off, then the face is washed with warm water and dried, and a light moisturizer applied.

Other Uses: Elder was popular in medieval folk medicine. The flowers, fruit and even the bark were used for colds, sciatica and rheumatism, as a diuretic, purgative, and to promote perspiration. The flowers and berries may be used to make delicious wine.

Sanicle

Umbelliferae

Sanicula europaea L.

Description: A perennial plant up to 40 cm high, with a short, trailing, blackish-brown rootstock producing an erect, simple, sharply angular stem. The basal leaves on long petioles are palmately divided into five parts, serrate. Small white or reddish flowers grow in compound umbels from May to July. The fruit is a globose achene densely covered with hook-shaped prickles, by which it is attached to a moving body which distributes it widely.

Origin and Distribution: Native to Europe, western Asia and northern Africa, but also found in the high mountains of tropical Africa. The plant prefers moist, humus-rich, shady woodland, especially mixed or deciduous, at various altitudes.

Harvesting and Preparation: The leaves of sanicle are gathered during the flowering period and dried as quickly as possible in shade.

Constituents: This species has not been fully investigated scientifically. It contains tannins and saponins (saniculagenins A−D), and also allantoin (0.2 per cent) which aids the healing of damaged tissue.

Cosmetic Uses: An infusion is recommended as a deodorizing gargle and mouthwash, for washing skin affected with acne and pimples, and as an ingredient of face packs used to remove impurities and unclog the pores.

Other Uses: The Latin name of the plant comes from the verb *sanare* − to cure − indicating that the species has long been used in medicine. It is found in most medieval herb collections and herbals, where it was considered a first-class medicinal plant. Both roots and herb were used for healing open wounds. In modern medicine it has been rather neglected, but is still frequently used in folk medicine.

Sandalwood

Santalum album L.

Description: A small to medium-high, evergreen tropical tree which lives as a semi-parasite on the roots of other plants, especially some bamboos and palms. It grows very slowly and has oval leaves covered with a whitish bloom, and small flowers in numerous clusters.

Origin and Distribution: Sandalwood comes from southwestern India (Mysore), from where it spread to the dry, high regions of the tropical zone (700−1,000 m above see level) with gravelly or rocky soils.

Harvesting and Preparation: Only trees 20−40 years old have fully developed, aromatic dark wood containing volatile oil. They are felled, the bark is removed and the trunks are exported in logs 90−120 cm long for further processing. The best wood is obtained from trees growing on poor, dry soil. Fresh wood is odourless; the scent only develops during the drying process.

Constituents: Sandalwood oil, extracted from the wood, is considered very important, especially for cosmetic purposes. It contains santalol, bisabolene, farnesol, isovaleraldehyde, isoborneol and other components.

Cosmetic Uses: The oil is used in various perfumes added to soaps and bath additives. Santalol and its compounds are added to face creams, lipsticks, skin lotions and powders, and santalol is the basic substance in many perfumes. Sandalwood oil is also widely used in the perfume industry; both santalol and sandalwood oil form part of Chanel No. 5. Another volatile oil with a sandalwood-like scent is that obtained from the Australian tree *Eucarya spicata*.

Other Uses: In the regions where sandalwood is grown, all parts of the plant are used in folk medicine for their astringent and disinfectant properties. Saw-dust from the heart of the tree is used to perfume chest-of-drawers and wardrobes. Throughout southeastern Asia and Japan fragrant sandalwood sticks are popular as incense in homes and for ritual purposes.

Soapwort
Saponaria officinalis L.

Caryophyllaceae

Description: A perennial plant up to 80 cm high, with a cylindrical, profusely branched rootstock about one finger thick. The erect, somewhat branched stems may be rough or smooth, and bear opposite, ovoid-lanceolate, rough-edged leaves. The flowers, approximately 3 cm in diameter, have a purple-tinged calyx and five white to pinkish petals, and are borne in clusters from June till September. The fruit is an oblong capsule with numerous seeds.

Distribution: Soapwort occurs in central and southern Europe, on river banks and along roadsides, railway embankments and waste places. It is sometimes grown in gardens, usually in its double-flowered form, but it can easily become a troublesome weed, tolerating considerable drought.

Harvesting and Preparation: The rootstocks with roots are gathered, washed quickly and dried in the sun or artificially at temperatures not exceeding 50° C.

Constituents: Its Latin name indicates that its main active substance is a mixture of saponins; the roots contain about 5 per cent, in a mixture called saporubin. *Gypsophilla paniculata,* a related species, contains up to 20 per cent saponins.

Cosmetic Uses: Soapwort is suitable for cosmetics in which foam is desirable, such as toothpastes, mouthwashes, soaps, shampoos and foam baths. If about a handful of the dried roots is extracted with half a litre of hot water, soap-like solution suitable for washing may be obtained. The South American rosaceous tree *Guillaia saponaria* contains approximately 10 per cent saponins in its bark (soap bark), which is used in the same way as soapwort.

Other Uses: In medicine, soapwort is administered internally for inflammations of the respiratory tract as an expectorant, and is also a mild diuretic.

Sesame

Pedaliaceae

Sesamum indicum L.

Description: An annual plant 80–110 cm high in subtropical conditions, 100–200 cm high in tropical conditions, forming a tuft of several branching stems. The ovoid to oval leaves, on long petioles, are of variable shape. Flowers rise from the leaf axils singly or in groups of two or three, and consist of a downy, tubular, bell-shaped corolla and a small calyx of five sepals. The corolla can be white, pink, red or violet. The fruit is an oblong capsule bearing rough, mat, flattened seeds which are white, yellow, brown or reddish.

Origin and Distribution: A very old cultivated oil plant of unknown origin. Probably native to Ethiopia, but according to some authorities it comes from Asia. Cultivated mainly in India, northern and eastern Africa, Syria and Egypt. Sesame will only grow in high temperatures.

Constituents: Sesame seeds contain on average 50 per cent semi-drying oil composed mainly of oleic and linoleic glycerides. It was possibly the earliest edible oil used, and is still obtained today by the relatively primitive method of cold expression.

Cosmetic Uses: Sesame oil is used in the manufacture of high-quality soaps, skin milks, creams and lotions and is added to shampoos and hair conditioners. In perfumery it is an important fat medium in 'enfleurage', that is, the method of extraction used for obtaining fragrances (such as those from mimosa or tuberose flowers) that cannot be distilled. Sesame bran, the ground press cake left after the oil is pressed from the seeds, contains 15 per cent oil, up to 40 per cent proteins and 22 per cent nitrogen-free substances. The cake is widely used cosmetically, in countries where sesame is cultivated, for cleansing dry skin.

Other Uses: Sesame oil has been used since ancient times (by Arabian and Indian doctors) in various medicinal preparations. Today it is used mainly in cooking, as an excellent edible oil that tastes similar to olive oil. The oriental sweet, *halva,* is prepared from ground sesame seeds, as is *tahina,* a paste widely used in Middle Eastern cooking.

Potato

Solanaceae

Solanum tuberosum L.

Description: A perennial plant with thin underground rootstocks on which tubers are formed; the tubers, potatoes, are filled with starchy reserve tissue, and are a staple source of starch in many parts of the world. The profusely branching stems bear alternate, unpaired-pinnate leaves. The five-petalled star-shaped flowers are white, blue or violet, with prominent yellow anthers. The fruit is a globose berry.

Origin and Distribution: The potato came originally from South America, where cultivated varieties were bred from wild species such as *Solanum andigenum*. It was introduced to Europe in the 16th century, and at first cultivated only in botanical gardens rather than as food. It was not until the beginning of the 18th century that their cultivation as an agricultural crop began in Europe, first of all in Germany. By the 19th century potatoes were being widely grown as a food crop, and for starch factories and distilleries.

Cultivation and Harvesting: Potatoes, grown as annuals, have numerous cultivated varieties. They reproduce by tubers or by seeds. When cultivated they are grown mainly from tubers, as it is only in this way that a variety will come true to type.

Constituents: All parts of the plant, including raw potato tubers, contain the toxic pseudoalkaloid solanin which is destroyed by boiling. The tubers also contain vitamin C and phenolic substances which darken when oxidized, but their main constituent is starch.

Cosmetic Uses: Potatoes are excellent for the preparation of a home-made paste for healing rough, chapped hands. Boiled potatoes are mashed with milk, and wheat flour is added to make a paste. This is applied to the skin and left on for 10 minutes before being washed off with warm water. Finally a moisturizing cream is applied. Potato starch is only rarely used in powders; its grains are larger than those of rice or maize starch and therefore less suitable.

Goldenrod

Compositae

Solidago virgaurea L.

Description: A perennial plant with a short rootstock and erect, round stem up to 1 m high, usually with a violet tinge in its lower part. The leaves are petiolate or sessile, alternate, elliptical and serrate. The golden-yellow flowers are arranged in racemes, and borne from August to October. The fruit is a hairy achene, about 4 mm long.

Distribution: Goldenrod is common throughout Europe, Asia and North America, where it grows in deciduous woodland and meadows, on sunny, sandy, rocky slopes at various altitudes.

Harvesting and Preparation: The flowering herb is gathered and dried in shade. The artificial temperature should not exceed 40° C. Sometimes the fresh herb and root are used.

Constituents: The flowering herb contains tannins, saponins, flavone glycosides and a small amount of volatile oil.

Cosmetic Uses: An infusion of the flowers and leaves (50 g to a litre of boiling water, extracted until cool, then filtered) is good for washing the face in cases of greasy skin with large open pores. A goldenrod infusion may also be used combined with the same amount of strong tea. Goldenrod baths tone up flabby muscles and skin; after taking such a bath every third day for a month, the skin usually noticeably improves, becoming rosy and firm, with contracted pores.

Other Uses: Flavone glycosides from goldenrod have been shown to reduce the fragility of blood capillaries, and the drug is used to treat progressive sclerosis in old age. The diuretic effect of the drug improves heart activity. Folk medicine recommends goldenrod baths for improving mobility after injuries and even after polio.

Clove

Myrtaceae

Syzygium aromaticum (L.) Merr. et Perry
syn. *Eugenia caryophyllata* Thunb.

Description: An evergreen tropical tree up to 20 m high with a dense, symmetrical, pyramidal crown. Its forked trunk has many lateral branches covered with smooth grey bark. In plantations it is usually cultivated to only 8–12 m in height. The ovate leaves are leathery, glossy, dark green above and paler below, with dot-like glands containing volatile oil. The flowers, growing in dense terminal clusters, are green at first, turning bright purple. The fruit is an oblong purple berry bearing a residual four-pointed calyx at the top. The spice – the familiar clove – is the dried unopened flower bud.

Origin and Distribution: Cloves come from the Molucca Islands which still produce the best-quality spice. However, the east African islands Zanzibar and Pembo now have the greatest share of the world market.

Constituents: The main active substance of cloves is the volatile oil (14–25 per cent), consisting mainly of eugenol (70–90 per cent), aceteugenol, humulene, caryophyllene, furfural and vanillin. There are negligible amounts of tannins, mucilage and resins in cloves. The composition of the volatile oil varies according to quality and place of origin.

Cosmetic Uses: The volatile oil has a disinfectant, anaesthetic and deodorant effect. It is made into perfumes used in the manufacture of toothpastes, mouthwashes, lipsticks, toilet soaps, hair oils, powders and deodorant sprays. It is also used to make perfumes of the carnation type and is therefore present in all cosmetics with this scent.

Other Uses: Clove is one of the most popular spices used in the kitchen. The eugenol in the volatile oil will anaesthetize tooth nerves and is also used as a disinfectant in the treatment of dental caries; a drop of clove oil dropped into a cavity will stop the pain of toothache.

Cocoa
Sterculiaceae

Theobroma cacao L.

Description: A tropical evergreen tree 5−8 m high, with a dense, globose crown. The young leaves are bronze-red, later deep green, oblong-oval, 15−20 cm long and tapering to a point. The small solitary flowers rise directly from the trunk and the base of the main branches; they are whitish, yellowish or pink. The fruit is a yellow-green, orange or brown pod up to 30 cm long, containing dark seeds called cocoa beans.

Origin and Distribution: Native to tropical South America but widely cultivated everywhere in the tropics, including south of the equator.

Cultivation and Preparation: Cocoa trees are cultivated in plantations; the beans are harvested from September to January (in the northern hemisphere). Cocoa beans are roasted and ground into powder and fat is obtained by hot pressing; this fat is called cocoa butter because at room temperature it has the consistency of butter. From the press cake and husks fat of poor quality is extracted.

Constituents: The cocoa butter contained in the beans (about 50−60 per cent) contains mainly glycerides of oleic, palmitic and linoleic acids. Cocoa beans also contain small amounts of caffeine and the alkaloid theobromine which has significant diuretic effects, regulates heart activity and relieves some blood circulation disorders.

Cosmetic Uses: Cocoa butter is used in the manufacture of moisturizing creams and powders for sensitive skin, being one of the neutral fats which do not irritate the skin. It is suitable for the preparation of pastes which are mixtures of powders with fat, such as grease paints, and for the manufacture of the best-quality lipsticks. It is used in the process of enfleurage to extract rare volatile oils from flowers.

Other Uses: Fermented, roasted cocoa beans are ground to powder from which a nutritious beverage − cocoa − is prepared. Large quantities are also made into chocolate. In pharmacy cocoa butter is used for the preparation of suppositories and other capsules containing medicines.

Wild Thyme

Labiatae

Thymus serpyllum L.

Description: A small, shrubby perennial plant with numerous stems which are slightly woody at the base and partly decumbent, partly erect. The stems, 10–30 cm long and 1 mm thick, are reddish and finely hairy. The small leaves, on short petioles, are ovoid to linear. The purple to pale pink or white flowers are arranged in small heads and appear from June till September. The fruit is a nutlet. The whole plant gives off a pleasant smell.

There are many species of thyme with numerous forms or subspecies, some of which have specific features and can be easily distinguished and some of which can be distinguished only with difficulty.

Distribution: Found throughout the temperate zone of the Old World, from India and Africa to Greenland and Iceland. Naturalized in North America. Abundant on dry sunny slopes, along roadsides and in thickets and woods.

Harvesting and Preparation: The herb is gathered shortly before or during flowering and dried as quickly as possible in shade or at artificial temperatures not exceeding 40° C. It is also used for the distillation of volatile oil which is employed for similar purposes as the herb.

Constituents: The flowering herb contains 0.2–0.6 per cent volatile oil of variable composition. The prevailing component is p-cymene, and it also contains thymol, carvacrol and citral which give the volatile oil its disinfectant properties. The presence of tannins and bitter substances in the volatile oil increases the oil's effect.

Cosmetic Uses: An infusion of the herb (100 g per litre of boiling water, extracted until cool) is used to promote blood circulation in tonic and disinfectant baths. It also forms part of some cosmetics used for improving the appearance of rough or greasy skin with large pores, and of hair rinses for greasy hair. The volatile oil is used in mouthwashes and toothpastes, for perfuming soaps and bath additives and can also be made into face lotions and creams, shampoos and cosmetics for men.

Other Uses: The antispasmodic effects of the volatile oil make it useful for treating gastro-intestinal problems, when it is drunk as a tea. Either the whole herb or the volatile oil may be used for inflammations of the upper respiratory tract and as a urinary and intestinal disinfectant.

Garden Thyme

Labiatae

Thymus vulgaris L.

Description: A perennial plant forming a low subshrub up to 40 cm high. The quadrangular stems are woody at the base, downy in their upper part. The leaves on short petioles are linear to elliptical, with rolled margins, and downy underneath. The small two-lipped flowers have a downy, bell-shaped calyx and violet or pink petals, and are clustered in groups of three to six in the leaf axils, forming terminal spikes. The flowering period is from May to June. The fruit is a nutlet.

Origin and Distribution: Native to the Mediterranean region, where it is abundant in uncultivated, dry rocky places. Grows best in warm areas but it is also successfully cultivated in gardens in cool, high regions.

Harvesting and Preparation: For pharmaceutical purposes common thyme is grown in field cultures in many different forms. The herb is gathered shortly before flowering, in dry weather, and dried as quickly as possible in shade. It has a spicy smell and pleasant, pungent taste.

Constituents: The flowering herb contains 0.5−2.5 per cent volatile oil, obtained by distillation with steam, and also tannins and bitter substances. The volatile oil has many components including thymol, p-cymene, carvacrol, α-pinene, linalool, borneol and cineole. The character and composition of the volatile oil depend on the variety cultivated and its place of origin. The main suppliers are southern France, Spain and Morocco.

Cosmetic Uses: The herb and its volatile oil have bactericidal effects, and are used in toothpastes, mouthwashes, sprays, gargles, aftershaves, disinfectant creams and skin lotions and bath additives. Thyme can also be used in small quantities (5 parts per 100) in herbal face packs; it is not recommended in larger quantities as it can irritate the skin, causing itching and swelling. As well as the herb and the volatile oil, pure thymol can be used cosmetically for its antiseptic action.

Other Uses: Thyme has been a well-known culinary herb and medicinal plant since ancient times. In modern medicine its bactericidal effects are employed in treatments for inflammation of the upper respiratory tract and for indigestion.

Small-leaved Lime, Small-leaved Linden

Tilia cordata Mill.

Tiliaceae

Description: A deciduous tree up to 30 m high with broad, heart-shaped leaves which are dark green above and lighter beneath with clusters of brown hairs, with finely serrate margins. The yellow flowers giving off a strong, pleasant smell are arranged in cymose clusters. The fruit is a spherical achene bearing a single seed.

Distribution: Found almost throughout the whole of Europe, as far north as southern Sweden. Abundant in lowland forests near rivers, and often planted in towns.

Harvesting and Preparation: The flower clusters are gathered when in full blossom, with the membranous bracts, and dried in shade. The drug must not lose its golden-yellow colour or be allowed to absorb moisture.

Constituents: The flowers contain flavone glycosides, farnesol and volatile oils (0.02 per cent), mucilages and other, little-known substances.

Cosmetic Uses: An infusion of the flowers has a favourable effect on the hair. Fresh or dried linden blossoms are infused (50 g to a litre of warm water, extracted for 30 minutes), diluted if necessary and used as a hair rinse. It makes the hair smooth, flexible and glossy, and smell of honey. Extracts of linden flowers are used in the manufacture of creams, lotions, bath additives and shampoos, as they protect sensitive skin against infection. Stabilized extracts are also manufactured.

Other Uses: Linden blossoms have long been known as an important drug because of their diaphoretic, diuretic and antispasmodic effects. Linden tea is useful for colds, sore throat and influenza. It is also an important melliferous plant. Its soft, light wood is used in woodcarving, for the production of excellent-quality charcoal and for numerous other products. It is also grown as ornamental tree in streets and gardens, and as a specimen tree.

Coltsfoot

Compositae

Tussilago farfara L.

Description: A perennial plant rapidly spreading by means of its creeping rootstock. From some rhizome buds flower-bearing stems arise, from others leaves. The downy, white, scaly flower stems are 10−15 cm long. The heart-shaped, toothed leaves appear after flowering, and form a rosette. The large yellow flowers, appearing in March and April, have marginal ray florets and tubular disc florets. The fruit is a hairy achene.

Distribution: Found almost throughout the whole of Europe, in western and northern Asia and the mountains of northern Africa. Abundant on damp clay soils, especially in clearings, on the banks of streams, in roadside ditches and fields. In some areas it becomes a troublesome weed.

Harvesting and Preparation: The flower-heads are gathered in early spring and dried quickly in shade. The leaves are gathered in May and June and dried in the sun. Care must be taken to distinguish them from the similar leaves of butterbur *(Petasites hybridus)* and various burdock *(Arctium)* species.

Constituents: The flowers and leaves contain large amounts of mucilages (7−8 per cent) and they are classified among mucilaginous drugs. The flowers also contain flavone compounds and substances of a carotenoid and tannin character.

Cosmetic Uses: Coltsfoot is used in emollient bath oils, face packs, creams, and face lotions for sensitive skin, as well as in preparations for deep cleansing greasy, blemished skin, and for dandruff. The fresh crushed or ground leaves can be used for the preparation of an excellent, non-irritating face pack for greasy and inflamed skin. The same face pack also has a favourable effect on healthy skin, making it look and feel rosy, firm and refreshed.

Other Uses: A coltsfoot infusion is one of the best herbal remedies for inflammations of the upper respiratory tract; this gave the plant its scientific name *(tussis* − cough). The drug may also be used externally for the treatment of inflammations, varicose veins, burns and insect bites.

222

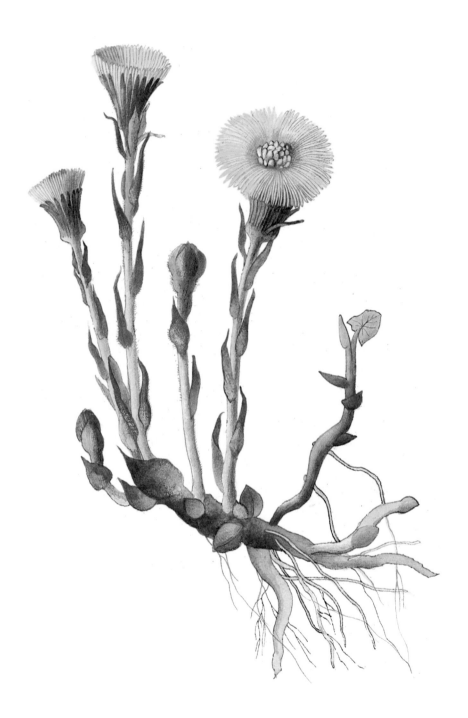

Stinging Nettle

Urticaceae

Urtica dioica L.

Description: A perennial plant with a profusely branched yellow rootstock, from which rise numerous quadrangular stems up to 120 cm high. The pointed leaves have serrate margins and long petioles. The small green flowers are arranged in hanging clusters growing from the upper leaf axils, and appear from June to September. Nettle is a dioecious plant: the flowers on female plants ripen into achenes. The whole plant is covered with stinging hairs.

Distribution: This species can be found throughout the whole of Europe, usually growing in communities in peaty, coniferous and deciduous woodland, at various altitudes. It is an abundant weed on rich soils in gardens, thickets and waste ground.

Harvesting and Preparation: Mainly the leaves from young flowering stems, or sometimes the whole herb, are gathered and dried immediately in thin layers in shade, at temperatures of up to 60° C, if possible without turning the leaves. The drug should retain its original green colour.

Constituents: The plant contains numerous substances which improve the general appearance and growth of the hair, including vitamins C, B_2 and B_6, histamine, chlorophyll A and B (which can easily be isolated from the plant), carotenoids and di- and triterpene alcohols.

Cosmetic Uses: Nettle has been thought to prevent the hair falling out. The prescription for a hair rinse is simple: 100 g of finely chopped nettle is poured over with half a litre of boiling water and, when cool, half a litre of 4 per cent vinegar is added. This preparation, warmed up, is used every day for ten days. The hair will visibly improve, becoming flexible and beautifully glossy.

Other Uses: Young nettles have always formed part of spring 'blood purging' cures and are either drunk as a tea or cooked and eaten like spinach.

Sweet Violet
Viola odorata L.

Violaceae

Description: A low perennial plant about 15 cm high with a short, thick rootstock and thin, trailing, rooting runners up to 20 cm long. The leaves, on long petioles, are circular-ovoid, with fine hairs and crenate margins. The violet, pedunculate flowers, appearing in March and April, are usually sterile, but in May inconspicuous, almost colourless, fertile flowers appear on the stolons near the ground. The fruits are globose, densely hairy capsules containing seeds.

Origin and Distribution: Native to the Mediterranean region, China and Japan. Probably not native to central Europe but naturalized after escaping into the wild from gardens, where it has been grown since time immemorial. Often found wild in deciduous peaty woodland, in hedges and on shrubby slopes.

Harvesting and Preparation: The rootstock or sometimes the whole plant is gathered when in flower. In France volatile oil is obtained from the flowers, and special varieties (Parma, Victoria and others) are cultivated for this purpose. Volatile oil is also obtained from the herb and rootstock. Undiluted volatile oil has almost no smell; its characteristic scent appears only when it is diluted.

Constituents: The scent is provided by the irone contained in the volatile oil. Irone scent is complemented by the presence of other substances such as benzylalcohol, eugenol and monadienal. The volatile oil is obtained by extraction of the flowers and leaves with petroleum ether, either in its liquid or solid state.

Cosmetic Uses: The delicate fragrance of violet is suitable for perfuming creams, lotions, cleansers, lipsticks, powders and other cosmetics. Violet also makes a lovely perfume: it consists of 4 basic substances, 17 nuancers, 7 effective and 6 fixing substances.

Other Uses: Violet can be used therapeutically for the preparation of cough syrup and, in the form of infusion, for headache. Sweet violet is no longer used for these purposes except, sometimes, in folk medicine; the wild pansy *(Viola tricolor)* is now more widely used instead, as a remedy for mucous congestion and as a diuretic.

Mistletoe

Loranthaceae

Viscum album L.

Description: An evergreen, semi-parasitic shrub about 60 cm high, with a short, forked stem. The branch segments are cylindrical, thickening and brittle at the nodes. The leathery yellow-green leaves are linear-lanceolate, stiff and smooth. It is a dioecious plant, with both male and female flowers green. From the female flowers white, spherical, pea-sized berries ripen, becoming mature in November and December.

Distribution: Occurs in the whole of southern and central Europe and northern Asia, where it grows on the trunks and in the tops of poplars, apple trees, firs, pines, etc. Its numerous sucking roots, called 'haustoria', penetrate the wood of the host tree and draw water from the wood along with dissolved mineral substances.

Harvesting and Preparation: Young twigs with leaves are harvested in December and January and dried very slowly at temperatures of up to 45° C. The unpleasant smell of the fresh plants almost completely disappears after drying.

Constituents: Mistletoe contains a poison called viscotoxin, a polypeptide composed of approximately 17 different amino acids. Its quality and quantity differs according to the host and the age of the plant.

Cosmetic Uses: Mistletoe extracts are used in combination with other plant extracts in creams and emulsions, for soothing irritated, sensitive skin. Besides their emollient effect, these preparations have disinfectant, anti-inflammatory and astringent properties. They close the pores, stop excessive sebum secretion and make chapped skin smooth. Mistletoe is also effective when used in shampoos for dandruff.

Other Uses: Recent experiments have shown that aqueous extracts of mistletoe contain substances slowing down tumour growth. There is still a long way to go from animal experiments to the employment of mistletoe in human medicine, but it is now the focus of a great deal of attention.

Index of Common Names

230

Index of Scientific Names

231